# Buildability in Practic

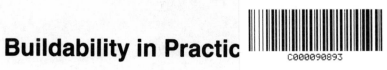

# Buildability in Practice

Ian Ferguson MA (Cantab), MSc (Manc), Dip Arch, ARIAS

Mitchell · London

*By the same author*
**Quality on Site**, Batsford 1986

© Ian Ferguson 1989
First published 1989

Typeset by Deltatype, Ellesmere Port
and printed in Great Britain by
Dotesios Printers Ltd, Trowbridge, Wilts

Published by the Mitchell Publishing Company Limited
4 Fitzhardinge Street, London W1H 0AH
A subsidiary of B T Batsford Limited

*A CIP catalogue record for this book is
available from the British Library*

ISBN 0 7134 5920 4

# Contents

# Introduction

Buildability can be defined as the ability to construct a building efficiently, economically and to agreed quality levels from its constituent materials, components and sub-assemblies. It should be separated conceptually from 'function and performance', which are concerned with the purposes, dimensions, weights, strengths, etc, of materials and components. Designers are familiar with function and performance, since almost everything which they draw or describe in writing at the 'production drawing' stage is intended to convey the quality which they wish to see achieved in the completed building. Yet the 'production' documents, a misnomer, since they are not explicitly concerned with production, do carry implicit references to how the building will be assembled and, when they are received by the contractor, they are examined carefully from this point of view. If the assembly process is likely to prove difficult, the contractor may draw this fact to the designer's attention, enabling him to reconsider the design. On the other hand, and this is where the client rightly becomes concerned, he may allow the unaltered design to proceed to site, relying upon his skills as a negotiator to recover the costs of inefficiency, or as a 'practical man' to solve the problems in situ as they arise. When designer and constructor work closely together from the beginning of a job, redesign may cause relatively few problems, but when a design is issued, supposedly complete, before the contract is let, any unforeseen complication in assembly will either have been allowed for in the contractor's price – long experience having taught him that this is wise – or its costs will be recovered later, using the various stratagems sanctioned by the contract. Either way, the client will pay.

Buildability is concerned with activities on site and, specifically, with sequences of operations and building method. It is about the dynamics of building, about the rough and tumble of building work and about the difficulties inherent in putting together a complex jigsaw of materials, components and sub-assemblies, often in bad weather and at all seasons of the year, when hands are frozen and legs are knee deep in mud. It is for these reasons, partly, that attempts have been made repeatedly over the years to transfer as much of the assembly process as possible to the factory. Yet, whatever the percentage of work carried out in this way, it will still be necessary to deliver the manufactured components and sub-assemblies to the site, to off-load them from delivery vehicles, to store them until they are needed and to place them in their correct positions in the building. Although this is largely an organisational problem, and one in which the constructor is, or should be, skilled, it will be apparent that the design of components and sub-assemblies can assist or hinder assembly and that hindrance will result both in delay and additional cost. This is even more the case when there has been little design rationalisation, when the building has to be assembled from large numbers of small components, rather than small numbers of large ones, when the interfacings and fixings between components are complex, or when the labour, tools, plant and equipment are mismatched to the tasks in hand. It can safely be concluded, therefore, that both designers and constructors, but especially the former, can radically affect the way in which a building is built and that 'getting it right' can only be beneficial, both to the quality of the completed building and to the client's pocket.

Since at least the middle of the nineteenth century, the design of buildings has been separated increasingly from their production and, worse still, professions have grown up or been established which have reinforced this division. The result has been the decay of craftsmanship and a growing misunderstanding by designers and constructors within the building industry of each other's roles. In no other industry is it seen as sensible to divorce the design of a product from its fabrication and it is expected, therefore, that the designers working in those industries will be as familiar generally with the relevant production processes as the fabricators are with the broad intentions of the designers. One cannot imagine the design for a new car, or even of a new toast-rack, proceeding without intimate and informative discussions at every significant stage of the design process between designer, production engineer and craftsman, as well as client, sales and marketing personnel. Yet in the construction industry, responsible for a huge expenditure within the Gross Domestic Product, architects continue to be educated and to practise separately and contractors to work apart, not only from architects, but from the other major professions which contribute to the building process, such as engineers, surveyors, building managers and clerks of works. That this apartness is less than it was, at least within larger and more enlightened firms, is due not so much to a desire to correct a manifest nonsense as to clients who, increasingly impatient with what they recognise as gross inefficiency, have begun to demand change. For too long, many of them feel, they have been forced to connive in an activity whereby buildings are expensively and lengthily designed and constructed, at no cost to the designers and constructors it may be said, since fees and profits are related to contract sums, and where the end result has fallen well short of perfection. Indeed, it would often be true to say that, where results have been good, this has been due less to the inherent rightness of the design than to the practice, after so many years highly refined, of 'getting round' problems on site, rather than of solving them properly during design. The purpose of this book, therefore, is to give a further impetus to the process of integration, which is at last beginning to take place, by introducing designers especially to the concept of 'buildability'. This is done firstly, by defining the principles which govern it and secondly, by exemplifying these principles in two ways: by examining the major determinants, such as design, cost, communication method, preparation, assembly technique and buildability in use, and by showing how these determinants may be applied to the design of a city centre office block and to a large housing development.

# 1  Principles

'Buildability' may be defined as the ability to construct a building efficiently, economically and to agreed quality levels from its constituent materials, components and sub-assemblies.

### Buildability as a key element in building production

The efficient and economical production of a building requires the logical organisation of the sequence of assembly, each activity in that sequence being made possible by a process which ensures that materials, components and sub-assemblies are delivered to site, handled, stored, converted and prepared ready for assembly into the building. To achieve efficiency and economy, the building organisation must ensure continuity of work by so managing labour, plant and equipment that the flow of materials, components and sub-assemblies into the growing building is maintained. Good buildability, assisted by efficient management, ensures that the assembly sequence is logical, that the building process can be followed easily and that the flow of materials, components and sub-assemblies can be maintained at an optimum rate.

'*Agreed quality levels*' have been defined in a companion volume.[1] They

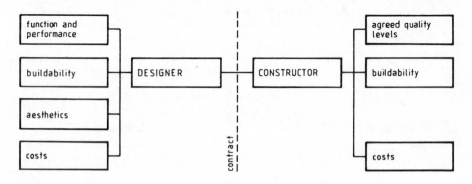

**1**

[1] *Quality on Site*, Ian Ferguson and Eric Mitchell, Batsford, London, 1986.

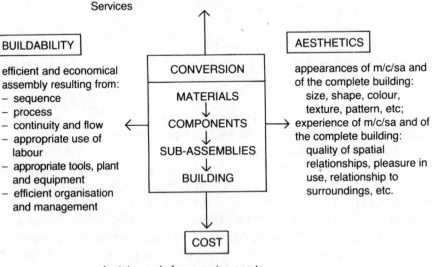

FUNCTION AND PERFORMANCE

Spatial organisation of building
   to fulfil functional purposes;
Physical characteristics of m/c/sa;
Strength and stability of m/c/sa;
Environmental performance of m/c/sa;
Services

BUILDABILITY

efficient and economical
assembly resulting from:
- sequence
- process
- continuity and flow
- appropriate use of
  labour
- appropriate tools, plant
  and equipment
- efficient organisation
  and management

CONVERSION

MATERIALS
↓
COMPONENTS
↓
SUB-ASSEMBLIES
↓
BUILDING

AESTHETICS

appearances of m/c/sa and
of the complete building:
   size, shape, colour,
   texture, pattern, etc;
experience of m/c/sa and of
the complete building:
   quality of spatial
   relationships, pleasure in
   use, relationship to
   surroundings, etc.

COST

of m/c/sa and of conversion one to
   the other[1]
of labour needed to design, manage
   and assemble the building, other
   than that of[1]
of tools, plant and equipment needed
   to assemble the building (other
   than[1]
of providing certain level of
   durability (life-cycle costs)

2

[1] *Quality on Site*, Ian Ferguson and Eric Mitchell, Batsford, London, 1986.

are the standards agreed between the building owner, the designer and, if possible, the constructor as being appropriate for that particular building. They include the criteria of 'function and performance' and 'aesthetics', and relate to 'cost' and 'buildability'. The positions of these criteria in relation to the design and construction processes are illustrated in diagram 1.

A building consists of materials, components and sub-assemblies. For the purposes of this book, it is assumed that components are made from materials and sub-assemblies from components; the building itself results from the bringing together of the sub-assemblies:

materials → components → sub-assemblies → building

The process whereby materials are transformed by a series of steps into the completed building is defined as 'conversion'. Conversion can take place either on or off the site, depending upon the nature of the materials, components and sub-assemblies, the labour, tools, plant and equipment needed to carry out the work and hence the organisation required:

off-site ← conversion → on-site

In addition to the building itself, the materials, components and sub-assemblies must satisfy the criteria of function and performance, buildability, aesthetics and cost if the agreed quality levels for the building are to be achieved. Diagram 2 lists the major characteristics of each criterion.

During conversion, 'interfaces' occur between the different materials, components and sub-assemblies, essentially at joints or nodes. These, too, must satisfy the criteria of function and performance, buildability, aesthetics and cost at the agreed quality levels for the building. Diagram 3 illustrates the concept of conversion:

COMPONENT (mortar) formed by
converting
MATERIALS (cement, lime, sand,
         water)

SUB−ASSEMBLY (wall) formed by
converting
COMPONENTS (bricks, blocks,
         mortar, ties etc )

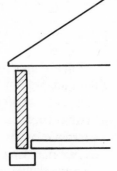

BUILDING formed by
converting
SUB−ASSEMBLIES (walls,
roof, floors, etc)

**3**

and diagram 4 that of interfaces:

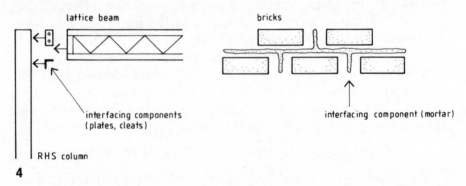

**4**

The joining of materials, components and sub-assemblies does not always require the addition of interfacing components, however. Materials, components and sub-assemblies have to be adapted so that joining is possible, but this can be achieved by omitting material or by altering specification, as well as by adding extra components. For example, cutting a component to size so that it will fit is a 'negative' adaptation, whereas altering a mortar type to ensure a good chemical bond is an adaptation by 'specification'. Diagram 5 illustrates these three possibilities:

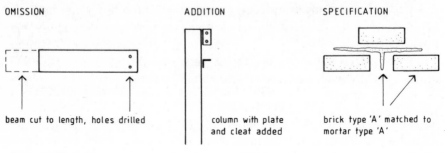

**5**

Final connection between components does not depend solely upon their adaptation, however. Whereas this ensures that a joint can be made, physical connection to ensure structural integrity requires the use of 'fixing' components. Once again, it is not always necessary to *add* such components: in addition to the use of bolts, screws, rivets and welds, for example, fixing can be effected either by so designing adjacent components that they lock together, or by achieving a chemical bond, as with glues or in the manufacture of concrete. ('Physical' bonds, such as those which rely upon magnetism, are ignored for present purposes.) Diagram 6 illustrates these alternatives:

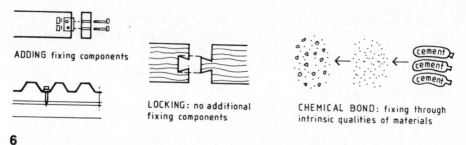

ADDING fixing components

LOCKING: no additional
fixing components

CHEMICAL BOND: fixing through
intrinsic qualities of materials

**6**

Good buildability is a major determinant of efficient and economical building production, which depends upon the bringing together of materials, components and sub-assemblies at point of assembly so that assembly into the growing building can take place with optimal efficiency. The ability to assemble logically, accurately and quickly does not depend solely upon this organisational competence, however, for if the components can not be fitted together, or if there is a bewildering variety of components which relate to each other in many different ways, or if the personnel have difficulty in carrying out the work, delays will occur and costs will rise. From this can be deduced a number of other principles upon which buildability crucially depends.

## Tolerances

If a building is to be assembled efficiently from its constituent materials, components and sub-assemblies, tolerances must exist between them and these must fall within acceptable limits. The mathematical basis of tolerances, 'tolerance theory', has been developed by the British Standards Institution in B5 5606, *Code of Practice for accuracy in building*[1] and in its supporting Draft for Development No 22: 1972, *Tolerances and Fits*. Transferring the principles enumerated in these documents to the issue of buildability, the importance of controlled tolerances can be demonstrated. In the following discussion, the term 'primary component' is used to differentiate two or more adjacent components from the interfacing and fixing components which may lie between them. Diagram 7(a) illustrates the preferred condition:

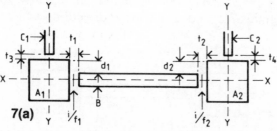

**7(a)**

[1] BS 5606 *Code of Practice for accuracy in building*. DD 22: 1972 *Tolerances and Fits*, both British Standards Institution.

Here, a primary component 'B', say a cladding panel, lies between two similar primary components 'A₁' and 'A₂', perhaps concrete columns. $A_1$ and $A_2$ are aligned along the 'x–x' axis and '$d_1$' equals '$d_2$'; '$t_1$' equals '$t_2$', these being the tolerances which permit component 'B' to fit between components 'A₁' and 'A₂' and which are wide enough to accommodate any necessary interfacing and fixing components, 'i/f₁' and 'i/f₂'. Primary components 'C₁' and 'C₂' represent internal partitions, which, ideally as here, are aligned along the 'y–y' axes of 'A₁' and 'A₂' and comply with equal tolerances '$t_3$' and '$t_4$'. Suppose now that excessive deviation occurs in the alignment of 'A₁' and 'A₂' along the 'x–x' axis:

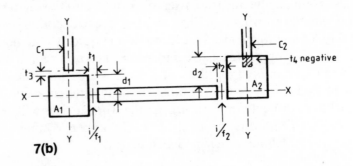

**7(b)**

Component 'B' still fits between 'A₁' and 'A₂', and interfacing and fixing components 'i/f₁' and 'i/f₂' can still be accommodated, but, because $d_2 > d_1$, the tolerance '$t_4$' has now been used up, with serious implications for buildability:

– beam connection 'A₁' to 'A₂' will be misaligned, affecting function and performance as well as the buildability of formwork, etc;
– additional work may be needed to the external face of 'A₂', owing to its new relationship to 'B';
– either 'C₂' will have to be shortened or, if both 'C₁' and 'C₂' have been shortened to make them the same, '$t_3$' will become excessively large, necessitating redesign of interfacing and fixing components between 'C₁' and 'A₁';

Similarly, where 'A₁' and 'A₂' are either too close together or too far apart (diagrams 7(c) and (d)), further difficulties will be caused:

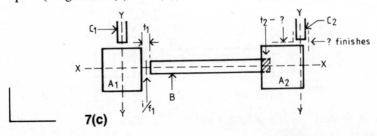

**7(c)**

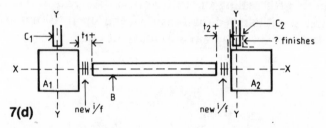

**7(d)**

In both cases, component 'B' will have to be adapted, if this is possible –
it may not be – or, if 't₁' and 't₂' have been reduced or enlarged, new
interfacing and fixing components may be required; the altered locations
of 'C₁' and 'C₂' in relation to 'A₁' and 'A₂' may also necessitate alterations
to internal finishes. In practice, gross deviations of the types shown are
unlikely to occur, except under the conditions noted later. More likely are
small but varying tolerances from bay to bay of the building, which only in
extreme cases result in the need for redesign or refabrication of the primary
components. On the other hand, all components are likely to change
slightly in relation to each other and it is important when designing for
good buildability to be aware of the allowable deviations in the positions of
components. This point is well covered in tolerance theory, but as the
example in Appendix 1 illustrates, it is difficult sometimes to achieve the
ideal in practice. Examining one of the junctions, that between primary
components 'A₁' and 'B' in more detail. Diagram 8(a) illustrates the
concept of allowable deviation:

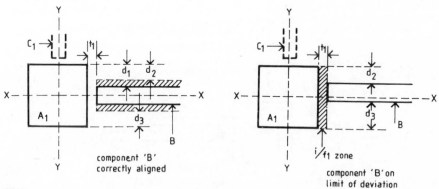

**8(a)**

The designed location of component 'B' is defined by '$d_1$', which relates
the position of 'B' to the inner face of 'A₁' in the direction of the 'y–y' axis;
'$d_2$' is the minimum tolerable distance of 'B' from the inner edge of 'A₁',
anything less requiring the alteration of finishes to the inner face of the
column. Similarly, 'B''s outward deviation is controlled by '$d_3$'. Note that
a further constraint on deviation is placed by the design of interfacing

component 'i/f$_1$': sealing the gap between 'A$_1$' and 'B' and achieving a secure fixing without redesign may depend upon 'B' not exceeding the allowable deviation. Diagram 8(b) illustrates this condition:

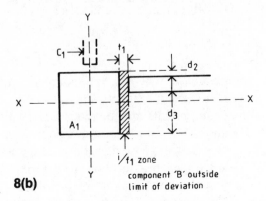

**8(b)**

Here, component 'B' is located well outside the allowable deviation represented by 'd$_2$' in diagram 8(a); 'd$_2$' has been reduced to the extent that 'B' is virtually aligned with the inner faces of 'A$_1$'. Similarly, 'd$_3$' has become excessively large. The practical effects are that major alterations to interfacing and fixing components 'i/f$_1$' and probably to internal detailing will be necessary. In fact, as already mentioned, all components are likely to move slightly in relation to each other and it is more useful in practice to understand the concept of a 'zone of deviation'. Diagram 8(c) illustrates this point:

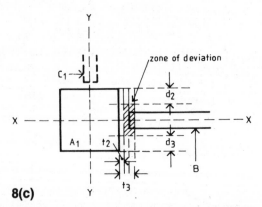

**8(c)**

Component 'B' can move in relation to 'A$_1$', or conversely 'A$_1$' in relation to 'B', within the allowable deviations defined by 'd$_2$', 'd$_3$', 't$_2$' and 't$_3$', without affecting the design of interfacing or fixing components or of any finishes. In effect, this means that all connections between primary components and the secondary components which depend on them must be designed on the assumption that a zone of deviation will exist and must be allowed for. A related point is that, whatever the deviation at a particular location, this may vary elsewhere, since constant deviations depend upon consistent alignment of components in relation to each other. Diagram 9 illustrates this problem:

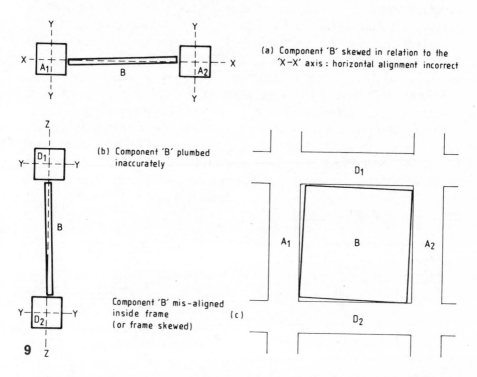

(a) Component 'B' skewed in relation to the 'X–X' axis : horizontal alignment incorrect

(b) Component 'B' plumbed inaccurately

Component 'B' mis-aligned inside frame (or frame skewed) (c)

9

Finally, tolerances are affected by differences in behaviour and buildability of materials, components and sub-assemblies which must be assembled adjacent to each other. For example, it is likely that lightweight concrete blocks will shrink as they dry unlike clay bricks, although these expand when heated; differing expansion coefficients must be accommodated, therefore, by the interfacing components and fixings if failure is not to occur. But more directly affecting buildability is the fact that it is impossible to assemble some components and sub-assemblies with the same accuracy as with others. For example, deviations of ±20 mm or more can occur in the plumbing of in situ concrete columns, compared with ±5 mm in precast columns and ±3–5 mm in factory made cladding units. It will be apparent, therefore, that a situation could occur in which the allowable deviation was grossly exceeded, when components of widely differing 'tolerance performance' were placed adjacent to each other and Appendix 1 describes just such an event. This explains why 'tolerance compatibility' is important if good buildability is to be achieved.

## Variety reduction

A large number of differing materials, components and sub-assemblies makes assembly difficult: all stages of the building process, delivery, handling, storage, preparation and final assembly, are compromised, risk of error is increased and delays occur. Personnel may have to learn many different assembly techniques or specialist personnel may have to be brought in. Tools, plant and equipment may proliferate or lie idle for periods of time until they are required. For these reasons, it is essential for designers to ensure that buildings are dimensionally co-ordinated,[1] are modular and that a system of preferred dimensions is used.[2]

Ideally, a building would be assembled from a pile of standard components and sub-assemblies, each of which was interchangeable with the other, the optimum being one universal component which would do all jobs everywhere in the building. This is impossible, but optima can usually be approached. For example, a building can be assembled from small, standard components such as bricks and blocks which, because of their size, can be combined at the scale of the wall and of the building itself to form unique sub-assemblies:

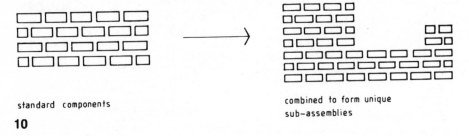

standard  components

combined  to  form  unique
sub—assemblies

**10**

In this case, the brick components have been converted into a wall sub-assembly by omitting some material (to form half bricks), by adding to their number and by incorporating such interfacing and fixing components as mortar and ties. This concept of achieving uniqueness by using the minimal number of different materials, components and sub-assemblies is important in buildability. It can be discussed under five headings: Conversion, Repetition, Handing, Handling and Dimensional co-ordination.

**(i) Conversion**   This can take place either off or on-site. In the factory, materials are converted into components and components into sub-assemblies using specialised labour, tools, plant and equipment. In this way, 'universal' materials, such as timber, are given 'unique' characteristics, such as a 't and g' profile; other examples are the firing of clay to

---

[1] BS 4330: 1968 *Controlling dimensions.*
[2] BS 4011: 1966 *Co-ordinating sizes for building components and assemblies.*

produce bricks of differing colours and strengths, and the rolling of metal sheets to form profiled metal cladding. On site, similar conversion processes take place, although usually on a more limited scale, and 'universal' materials and components are converted into 'unique' components and sub-assemblies during the preparation stages, prior to final assembly. Diagram 11 illustrates these processes:

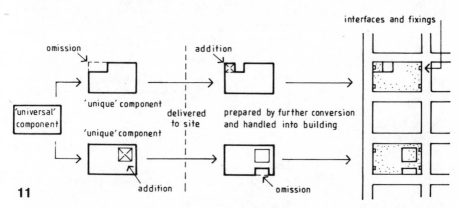

**11**

It will be apparent that every time work is carried out on a component to enhance its uniqueness, the variety of different components is increased. It is a prime objective of buildability to reduce this variety, by minimising the amount of conversion which must take place, especially on site.

**(ii) Handing**   Uniqueness in a component or sub-assembly is affected by the 'handing' of its physical characteristics, that is the imbalance of the distribution of the elements of the components within its overall shape. For example, an asymmetrically placed window opening in a cladding panel makes the handing of that component critical. The point is illustrated in diagram 11, but it can be demonstrated theoretically by means of the 'three-axis concept'. See diagram 12(a) overleaf.

The objective of universality can be most nearly achieved when the handing of a component is uncritical along all axes, as in component type 'B'; this is the great virtue of bricks and blocks which, although small in size, can be assembled in a variety of different positions. The larger the component, the more important becomes the 'handing', since the penalty for error is greater and since method and order of 'handling' are critical (see p. 25). In diagram 12(a), for example, component type 'D' can be assembled in a number of different positions in the building, as long as it is the right way up and not back to front. Component 'E', on the other hand, is highly specific in location and can be assembled only in those locations where an opening in the top left-hand corner is required. For this reason, the likely degree of repetition is limited. This would not be so if the

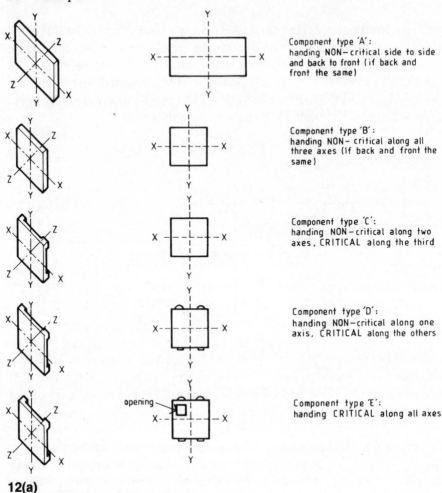

Component type 'A':
handing NON—critical side to side and back to front (if back and front the same)

Component type 'B':
handing NON— critical along all three axes (if back and front the same)

Component type 'C':
handing NON—critical along two axes, CRITICAL along the third

Component type 'D':
handing NON—critical along one axis, CRITICAL along the others

opening

Component type 'E':
handing CRITICAL along all axes

**12(a)**

opening was moved onto the centre-line of the 'y–y' axis (diagram 12(b)(ii)):

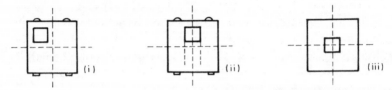

(i)          (ii)          (iii)

moving window position reduces variety and increases repetition

**12(b)**

Notice that the exact position of the window opening along the 'y–y' axis is immaterial, since the component can only be fixed one way up. If seating and handling were possible either way up, maximal repetition and variety reduction would be achieved by locating the window centrally, at the intersection of the axes (iii).

**(iii) Handling**   The greater the variety of components, the more problems are caused during the preparation stages, in ensuring that the right components arrive at the workplace in the right order. Of high significance here is the handling of components into position in the building. For example, assuming that the components in diagram 12(a) represent precast concrete panels, these, if different from each other, must be loaded onto the delivery vehicle in the correct order for off-loading and transferring into the building, on the principle usually of 'last on, first off'. 'Handing' of components is important in establishing 'handling' precedence: not only must wholly different components arrive at the workplace in the correct order of assembly, this principle must also apply at the more detailed level, where the only difference between two components is that their common features are handed. Door-sets are an example of this.

**(iv) Repetition**   Once the variety of materials, components and sub-assemblies in a building has been reduced to a minimum, consistent with the satisfaction of other design criteria, the frequency of use of these materials, components and sub-assemblies must be maximised. The reasons for this are to do both with the organisational process necessary during the preparation and assembly stages and with the refinement of design solutions, especially at interfaces. Personnel work more efficiently once they understand properly the tasks they are to perform; tools, plant and equipment can be matched accurately to the work, and interfaces can be thoroughly designed. The fundamental principle underlying interface design is that conversion should take place wherever it can be done most efficiently: complex components requiring specialised assembly skills, off-site in the factory and straightforward assembly, perhaps using lower order skills, on site. Diagram 13 illustrates how repetition can be practised on the simple joint analysed in Appendix 1 (diagram A1/4):

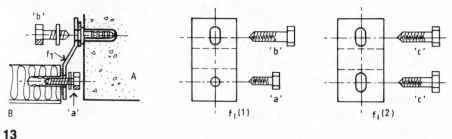

**13**

The joint consists of two primary components, 'A' and 'B', assembled to each other using an interfacing component, '$f_1$', and bolts 'a' and 'b' with spacers. '$f_1$' is assembled to 'B' off-site in the factory and, as long as the use of both 'a' and interfacing component '$f_1$' is standardised (minimal variety) in relation to the range of assembly operations carried out in that factory, the shapes, sizes and positions of the fixing holes are immaterial. On site, too, only one bolt 'b' is needed to complete the fixing to 'A'. Should 'f$_1$' be fixed to both 'A' and 'B' on site, however, the constraints of variety reduction work differently. Separate versions of 'f$_1$' would be needed for, although handing could be accommodated, as when 'B' is fixed to either side of 'A', the bracket would not be reversible: the slotted hole would no longer be accessible for adjustment purposes, and two differing sizes of bolt would be required. To achieve minimal variety and maximal repetitions of 'f$_1$' and its fixing bolts, a universal bracket, 'f$_1$(2)', is needed, with slotted holes at each end and bolts 'c' of equal length: the bracket can now be handed and reversed and as with the factory assembly, only one length of bolt is needed. Another problem occurs when several differing components have to interface with a standard component or sub-assembly: each component may have its unique interfacing and fixing components lying between itself and the sub-assembly, requiring alterations not only to the interfacing and fixing components but also to the labour, tools, plant and equipment required to assemble them. Diagram 14(a) illustrates this problem:

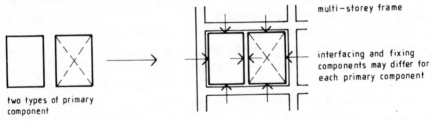

two types of primary component

multi–storey frame

interfacing and fixing components may differ for each primary component

**14(a)**

Two differing primary components, for example, a solid and a glazed panel, are required to fit into a bay of a multi-storey framed building. The beam and column faces are standard throughout, but adaptation of the primary components may be necessary to enable secure fixing to the frame to take place. If this is done by adapting either the beam and column faces or the primary components, the variety of beams, columns and panels is increased, perhaps expensively, and less repetition is possible. If, on the other hand, a common interfacing component is interposed between the primary components and the frame, the new 'combined' primary component can be repeated more generally throughout the building (diagram 14(b)).

Further demonstrations of this principle are the variety of doors possible within a standard frame, or the window frame of standard size and section containing differing combinations of fixed and opening lights.

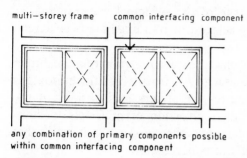

multi-storey frame    common interfacing component

any combination of primary components possible
within common interfacing component

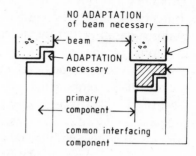

NO ADAPTATION
of beam necessary

beam

ADAPTATION
necessary

primary
component

common interfacing
component

**14(b)**

**(v) Dimensional co-ordination** In addition to simplifying the materials, components and sub-assemblies in a building, to reducing their variety and to ensuring the maximal repetition of this reduced variety, buildability is enhanced if components and sub-assemblies are related to each other according to a set of geometrically and dimensionally co-ordinated principles. Where these apply, limitations are imposed on the ranges of sizes within which components and sub-assemblies are available, which means, in effect, that variety is reduced and greater repetition is possible: if components must observe a range of preferences ranging in four steps from 25–300 mm, a multitude of variations is eliminated. To gain maximal benefit from this discipline, however, a number of constraints must be respected and these are set out in such documents as BS 4330: 1968,[1] BS 4011: 1966[2] and the later BS1 DD 51: Section 7: 1977.[3] For example, if a sheet component is supplied in standard sizes based on multiples of 600 mm, this module will dictate the spacing of the supporting structural members and even of plan size and floor to ceiling heights if cutting to waste is to be minimised. Thus a plasterboard sheet of 2400 × 1200 mm suggests that floor to ceiling heights should be 2400 rather than 2350 and that plan sizes should at least be multiples of 300 mm and preferably of 1200 mm. This is easier to achieve with 'closed' building systems, where all significant components and sub-assemblies can be designed together and manufactured to fit, than with 'open' ones, where the designer can select from the whole range of products available on the market. The benefits of dimensional rationalisation are marked: fewer different products need to be ordered, stored and handled, less adaptation is needed during the preparation stages and the rate of assembly can be increased – in addition to the elimination of much waste.[4] In other words, buildability can be substantially improved.

[1] BS 4330: 1968 *Controlling dimensions*.
[2] BS1 DD 51: Section 7: 1988 *Guidance on dimensional co-ordination in building*.
[3] BS 4011: 1966 *Co-ordinating sizes for building components and assemblies*.
[4] Skoyles E R, Skoyles R S *Waste prevention on site*, Batsford, London, 1987.

## Summary

Buildability may be regarded as one of the principal determinants in building design. Once the quality levels for the building have been agreed in terms of the criteria of function and performance, buildability, aesthetics and cost, the buildability element is examined in relationship to the materials, components and sub-assemblies from which the building is assembled. This examination requires an understanding that, in the progression towards final assembly, conversion of materials to components to sub-assemblies takes place, whether on- or off-site, and that conversion requires adaptation of the materials, components and sub-assemblies, either by addition, omission or change in specification. Where addition is necessary, special interfacing components are used and in most cases it will be essential to use fixing components to form the joint during assembly. Finally, although efficient organisation can secure a flow of the appropriate materials, components and sub-assemblies to the workplace, together with sufficient labour, tools, plant and equipment to complete assembly, good buildability requires in addition that the principles of tolerances, variety reduction, dimensional co-ordination and modular design and repetition are observed.

# 2 Designing for Buildability

Having established the principles upon which buildability depends, the next step is to examine how designers can best apply them in practical situations.

Designers must take into account factors other than buildability in their work: diagram 2 illustrates the connection between the dynamic processes of conversion from materials to the building itself and the four main criteria of function and performance, buildability, aesthetics and cost. At the least, even when the other three criteria are seen as being of paramount importance in a design, the designer should be aware of the production process; at best, he must understand how to integrate the four criteria, giving each one its due importance in the design.

The characteristics of the production process have been described by Bishop,[1] who identifies the task of production as 'the attempt to create iterative processes, so that benefit can be gained from hard-won experience'. In product manufacture, where large numbers of similar components are to be produced, design and development follow well understood paths. For example, initial design is tested both on paper and in mock-ups, proceeds to the prototype stage or to pilot production, is monitored for faults and is then revised before full production is commenced. The advantage that the product designer has is that refinement of the product can proceed during its early lifetime, so that by the time the 'de-bugging' phase is complete, a well 'sorted' product is being manufactured. This luxury of progressive refinement is denied apparently to the building designer. It is a common complaint of the architect, for example, that his building must be 'right first time', the underlying assumption being that this is an impossibility, since only with certain building types, such as low-cost housing and factory sheds, is the repetition possible which enables refinement to be achieved. The architect pleads further that his or her client demands a 'unique' solution, thereby preventing any possibility of standardisation, justifying this complaint by reference to differing sites, clients, briefs and social and peer group pressures. The preceding chapter has explained, however, that, even

[1] Bishop, D.: 'Buildability: the criteria for assessment'; Paper No. 45; Chartered Institute of Building, 1985.

where unique solutions are sought, these can be achieved by practising the repetition of a limited range of materials, components and sub-assemblies (diagram 10). Unfortunately, the construction industry has long been accustomed to assembling inefficiently designed buildings, to the extent that the ability to reach 'ad hoc' decisions on site is regarded with some pride: it is seen as a challenge to management and to craft skill. There is a point, however, at which even the ingenuity of the skilled contractor becomes overtaxed and it is at this point that delays occur and costs rise. The point shifts according to the level of skill being applied to the work and to the performance of the tools, plant and equipment available, but it is nevertheless the designer's responsibility to ensure that this point is never reached because his designs are difficult or impossible to assemble. The fact that there are disincentives to achieving efficient and economical designs, whether these are 'custom and practice' or a fee structure which actually encourages high costs, is no excuse when resources are limited and the client pays.

## Site buildability

The choice and type of site crucially affect buildability. A level, 'greenfield' site with good loadbearing soil is a different proposition from a city-centre one, with old basement structures and surrounding buildings. There are several important factors to be considered, apart from the design of the building itself: access to the site, whether free or obstructed, the availability of services, conditions below ground level and degree of slope, the position and size of surrounding buildings, noise and space for temporary works and storage areas.

**(i) Access**    If unusually difficult, access routes can prevent the use of bulky items of plant and the delivery of large sub-assemblies, such as steelwork, boilers and of air-handling equipment. Cranes, unless mobile, are delivered in sections by lorry and mobile cranes themselves, which may be needed to assemble the fixed cranes, must be able to negotiate bends and narrow roads. On very cramped sites, where storge space is limited or unavailable, frequent cartage is likely and this may necessitate the closing of public highways and the setting up of one-way systems. On waterlogged sites, on the other hand, storage areas must be accessible to plant without it getting bogged down. In extreme circumstances, it may be necessary to modify the design of the building or even to abandon the site altogether. Diagram 15 illustrates some of the constraints:

The original access, 'A', is impossible for large vehicles. A new access 'B' would be satisfactory, but better still would be dual accesses 'B' and 'C' permitting one-way working; the location of 'C' would depend upon the

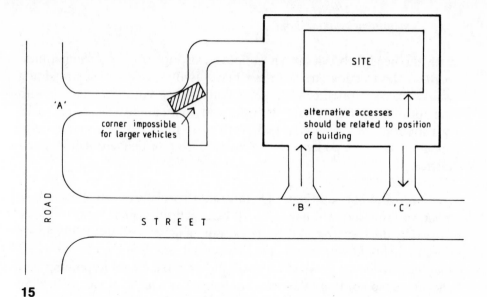

Inside the diagram:

SITE

'A'

corner impossible
for larger vehicles

alternative accesses
should be related to position
of building

'B'          'C'

R O A D

S T R E E T

**15**

design of the building and whether or not there were obstructions outside the site.

**(ii) Services**   The requirement for both temporary and permanent services during building is well understood. Efficient site buildability, however, demands their provision in such a way that building assembly is not impeded. For example, temporary services are required from Day 1 until completion, including water, electricity, drainage and communications, with fuels needed for certain periods. The permanent services, on the other hand, must be phased in to match the sequence of assembly, for example to permit excavation of foundations and the testing of water and gas systems, and to avoid interference with scaffolding, site transit handling and the work of the finishing trades.

**(iii) Work below ground level**   Before design begins, it is essential to obtain a clear understanding of the conditions likely to be met with below ground level, since the location, form and extent of the building may be fundamentally affected. Once the necessary data is gathered, design can proceed, but during the design process the designer should be aware of the problems he may be creating for the contractor during the excavation and 'below datum' stages. For example, labour type and quality, plant type and programming will be affected by the workability of the site: should excavators be tracked or rubber-tyred, will temporary roads be needed, how much cartage will be necessary, is part of the site likely to be polluted with chemical waste? Special plant may be needed, for terracing, piling and consolidation and as this is bulky, expensive and usually sub-contracted, the problems of access (i), contract method and site organisation, arise. A special problem is often posed by basements, beginning with the need to break out and remove existing structures. Sometimes, parts of the existing structure can be re-used, for example as retaining walls, but more often considerable excavation is required, together with the forming of new retaining walls and foundations. This can make working on tight sites cramped, with little room for plant, storage of materials and components or the manoeuvring of delivery vehicles and lorries.

**(iv) Surrounding buildings**   On infill and especially on city-centre sites, adjacent buildings will have to be protected from damage and nuisance caused by dust, noise and the interruption of access and services. During design, it should be remembered that special temporary works and plant may be needed to prevent collapse, for example by underpinning and shoring, or to minimise the risk of nuisance, by using electric rather than diesel motors to power plant for example, and by carrying out certain bulky deliveries at weekends. The erection and dismantling of fixed cranes are examples of 'out of hours' operations. Order of assembly and buildability can be affected by the nature and extent of the surrounding buildings: access, storage areas and plant may have to be located in such a way that the optimal sequence of assembly is compromised. For example, where an adjacent party wall must not be disturbed during building operations, the order of erection of a steel frame may have to change; or again, the swing of the crane jib dictate where the crane is located, this affecting the assembly sequence.

**(v) Temporary works and storage areas**   The space occupied by shoring, scaffolding, formwork, plant, compounds and workshops can be considerable. Their efficient location and distribution is necessary for good buildability and the designer should recognise this when considering both the utilisation of the available site area and the phasing of building assembly. For example, on congested sites, fully occupied by the buildings, adjacent streets may have to be closed to provide storage compounds, scaffolding and offices may straddle the pavements and it may not be possible to locate the tower crane sensibly anywhere. (This problem is dealt with fully in chapter 6.) It may also be necessary to complete part of the building and dismantle some of the temporary works before other parts can be started.

### The building: designing for practical assembly

It is important for designers to be aware of what is practicable assembly within the constraints of time and cost. This is determined by three major factors: the nature of the materials, components and sub-assemblies, the skills of the personnel and the type and suitability of tools, plant and equipment.

**(i) Materials, components and sub-assemblies**   One way of illustrating how materials, components and sub-assemblies can be put together in a practical way is by assuming a 'hierarchy of difficulty' of assembly, from 'impossible' to 'easy', and by studying examples of each. Five steps in the hierarchy an be identified:
  (1) Assembly impossible
  (2) Assembly only possible with extreme difficulty
  (3) Assembly possible but difficult
  (4) Assembly straightforward but perverse
  (5) Assembly easy
An additional factor is the ease or difficulty of maintaining the building during its life, its 'buildability in use', dealt with in chapter 8.

(1) *Assembly impossible*   A component can be assembled in such a way that subsequent dismantling is impossible: when it fails, the whole component must be replaced. Alternatively, a component can be designed so that any parts likely to fail can be replaced without the whole component having to be discarded. For example, a window should be designed in such a way that the glass can be replaced easily, but not so that the frame can be dismantled. When components are supplied to site in 'knock-down' form, it is essential that assembly is possible within the constraints imposed by adjacent components and that later replacement of parts likely to fail can take place.

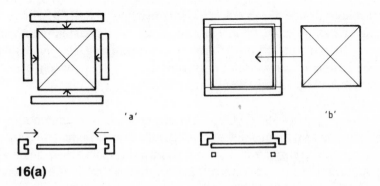

'a'          'b'

**16(a)**

In diagram 16(a), 'a' represents a frame and panel assembled in one operation: the panel is inserted in grooves in the frame and both it and the frame members are fixed together in one operation; 'b', on the other hand, represents a frame which is assembled before the panel is inserted, the panel being retained by beads. Whereas component 'a' could be assembled initially from the 'knock-down' set of five parts, were the frame to be supplied already assembled subsequent insertion of the panel would be impossible, as would its replacement; insertion and removal of the panel in 'b', on the other hand, presents no problem.

(2) *Assembly only possible with extreme difficulty*   A commoner failure during design is that of not visualising and understanding the likely sequence of assembly of a series of components, with the result that assembly becomes extremely difficult for the constructor.

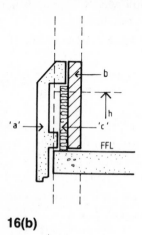

**16(b)**

Diagram 16(b) represents a section through a precast concrete cladding panel 'a', with a blockwork backing panel 'b' supporting a layer of loose insulation 'c'. The precast panel is fixed first, followed by the blockwork; the insulation is inserted behind the blockwork as this is raised. Unfortunately, once the blockwork has reached height 'h' above floor level, it is not possible to insert any more of the insulation. Various solutions include attaching 'c' to 'a', re-specifying 'b' as insulating blockwork, injecting a beaded cavity fill into the space between 'a' and 'b', and carrying 'c' up to cill level behind 'a'.

(3) *Assembly possible but difficult*   Handling heavy components into an opening by moving them sideways is difficult. Not only may tolerances be a problem – the components may not fit into the space (diagram 9) – but crane operation requires great skill, scaffolding can get in the way and the safety of personnel can be imperilled.

Diagram 16(c) illustrates that face fixing of such components is much more straightforward: whereas panel 'a' has to be lowered and then pulled into position, with the risk that it may swing back taking the operatives with it, panel 'b' is simply lowered close to the building face, edged slightly

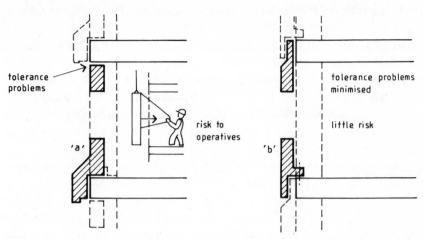

**16(c)**

inwards and secured to the fixing brackets. This method also solves the tolerance problems described in chapter 1 (diagrams 7–9).

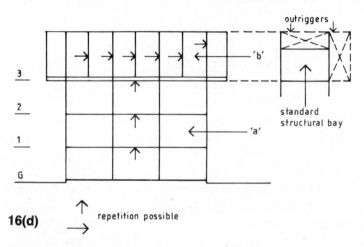

**16(d)**    ↑ → repetition possible

(4) *Assembly straightforward but perverse*    Diagram 16(d) represents a not unusual 'architectural' solution, in which a multi-storey framed building consists of two major structural sub-assemblies, one on top of the other. Each sub-assembly may in itself be straightforward to assemble, but when each is interfaced with the other, the following buildability problems arise:

– assembly will proceed with increasing speed and confidence up to level 3, owing to repetition and to the resulting understanding by the operatives of the assembly sequence;

– at level 3, new interfacing and fixing components for sub-assembly 'b' will be required, delaying progress;

– sub-assembly 'b' is a quite different structure from sub-assembly 'a':

new assembly techniques will have to be learnt and progress will be slow, despite repetition laterally;
– because of the slow structural assembly, following work, especially the cladding, will be delayed;
– site organisation is made more complex, owing to the need for additional materials, components and sub-assemblies and their storage and handling, for labour of different types and skills and for new tools, plant and equipment.

It is desirable, therefore, when variety of the type illustrated is required, to rationalise the structure in such a way that repetition is still possible. For example, had the overhang on level 3 been achieved by attaching 'outriggers' to the structural system used on levels G-2, rather than by changing it completely, minimal disruption to the working method would have occurred.

(5) *Assembly easy*    One of the easiest and most buildable assemblies is illustrated in diagram 16(e):

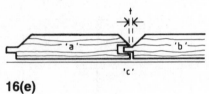

**16(e)**

Timber components 'a' and 'b' are converted off-site into standard widths, depths and profiles, thereby complying with the principles of variety reduction and repetition. Cutting to length is easy using simple tools and the joint is self-correcting for alignment, assuming a level backing 'c'. Furthermore, a relatively wide tolerance 't' is acceptable without affecting the integrity of the joint.

Initial assembly is only part of the problem: buildings have a lifetime during which they must be maintained and have any defective parts replaced. 'Buildability in use' is discussed in chapter 8, but it is important even during the early stages of the design process to consider ease of maintenance and replacement. The cleaning and maintenance of a building's exterior surfaces is well understood and is provided for by such means as gantries, cradles and mobile 'cherry pickers', but it is sometimes forgotten that bulky and complex items of plant, such as boilers and control gear, will probably have to be replaced several times during a building's life and that access to them can become difficult or impossible. Diagram 16(f) illustrates a framed building in which boilers, chillers and air handling equipment have been installed in a basement plant room:

Whereas initial installation, carried out as the frame rises, is relatively

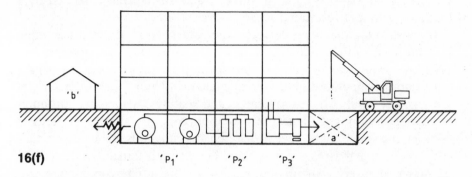

**16(f)**          'p₁'          'p₂'        'p₃'

straightforward, the replacement of the boilers 'p₁' is impossible after the building is complete: they can be moved neither to the left, owing to the presence of building 'b', nor to the right into access area 'a' owing to the presence of plant 'p₂' and 'p₃'. They must therefore be dismantled and reassembled in situ, a long and costly procedure.

In designing for the practical assembly of materials, components and sub-assemblies, it is important for the designer to be fully aware, not only of what is practicable assembly, but also of how to balance the claims of buildability against those of function and performance, aesthetics and cost. For example, although buildability may dictate that one constructional system is adopted consistently throughout the building, economy may dictate the reverse. Alternatively, clients may insist upon high quality finishes of many different varieties, thereby prejudicing the possibility of efficient repetition.

Although the conflict between buildability and economy should not develop if the principles of buildability are being observed, in practice it may be impossible to avoid. An example of this is where dissimilar primary components are interfaced, thereby requiring elaborate interfacing and fixing components to achieve the joint. Diagram 17 illustrates a common circumstance, where a timber panel wall becomes a masonry

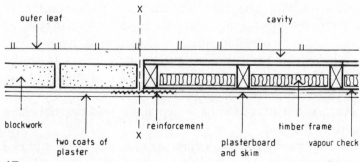

**17**

wall. This can happen where a timber frame structure is extended by a masonry structure forming cladding, garages, etc.

Because of the risk of movement either side of 'x–x', the interface must be reinforced and skim-coated. This work involves three separate trades, bricklayer, woodworker and plasterer, the plasterers having to perform fairly complex operations at different times using four different materials: render coat, wallboard, reinforcement and floating coat or skim. Although initial appraisal might suggest this solution, a careful analysis of the true costs of the joint might reveal that the building was better assembled entirely either in masonry or in timber. The example illustrated should not be taken to imply that all joints between dissimilar components are unacceptable, however. Some such joints are essential, as when glass is fixed into a window frame.

The potential conflicts between aesthetics and buildability are many and varied. For example, where several different materials or components are specified, production, and especially buildability, are affected because the building process and sequence are made more complex and because more interfaces and fixings will occur. Furthermore, rare or costly materials will often be supplied in small quantities, requiring special skills and tools to convert them without risk of waste or damage. For optimal buildability, therefore, designers should avoid the use of such materials and achieve their visual effects by using widely available and easily converted materials, which can be worked quickly and economically within the trade skills, tools, plant and equipment likely to be readily available.

Knowing where to deploy aesthetic sensibility is as important to the architect as is control of cost. It is not always necessary to achieve a visually perfect fit, for example, since much assembly is concealed behind surface finishes. The fit should, ideally, achieve perfect buildability, but this is not the same as ensuring that this is visually apparent. Both time and money can be wasted in achieving a high standard of finish in areas of the building which will never be seen and for this reason the concept of 'zones of visual acceptability' is useful. Diagram 18(a) illustrates the concept:

In the house section and the section through the Roman wall, areas 'a' will rarely or never be seen and assembly in these areas can proceed by the most direct methods regardless of appearance – unless an aesthetically purist line is being taken – provided that the constraints of function, performance and cost are being observed. Areas 'b' and 'c', on the other hand, lie within the zone of visual acceptability and assembly here must have regard to that fact.

When a designer feels that a major aesthetic objective is to make the interfaces or junctions in his building explicit, major buildability prob-

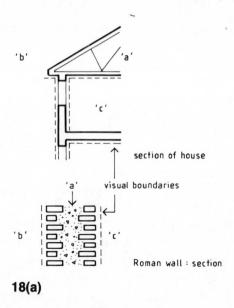

18(a)

lems can arise. For example, visually intersecting planes, in which any frame is suppressed and the sensation of solidity is removed, can be difficult to assemble. Diagram 18(b) illustrates a situation in which a glass wall meets the underside of a flat roof:

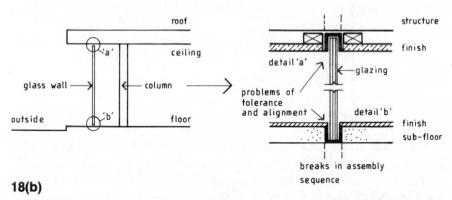

18(b)

The repetition possible in fixing the floor and ceiling finishes is interrupted by the assembly activities required to fix the glass wall in position. Since the joints are not concealed, great accuracy is required, both to align the glass and to ensure that the concealed frame edge is level with the outer faces of the finishes. In addition, the glass will be difficult both to fix initially and to replace (see diagram 16(a)). A commoner example of the same problem is where plasterboarded walls and ceilings meet: it is almost impossible to achieve a visually acceptable joint, which is why a cornice is essential. The cause of buildability is served whenever junctions are concealed since the critical eye can then be deceived. In diagram 18(c), a simple junction between structural post and beams can be located either side of the visual boundary:

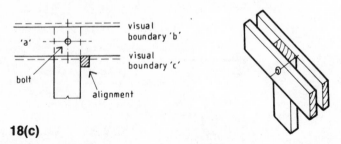

**18(c)**

When the joint is made with the visual boundary at 'b', the alignment of post and beam must be perfect, with the bolt central and tightened just enough so as not to bruise the timber; the timber itself must be well finished and possibly decorated. When the joint is made with the boundary at 'c', on the other hand, the area 'a' is concealed and the joint can be much rougher, the only exceptional buildability requirement being that the bottom edges of the beams are finished level and smooth to take the surface finish. Familiar examples of the same problem are illustrated in diagram 18(d):

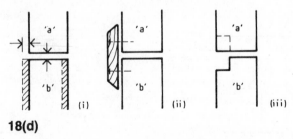

**18(d)**

A neat butt joint between 'a' and 'b' (i) is almost impossible to achieve, since the gaps and misalignments shown by the arrows can rarely be eliminated; solutions are shown in (ii) and (iii): either to use a cover bead, or to groove one corner of 'a' and 'b', using the shadow line to create a positive visual break.

Sometimes a designer wishes to achieve a visual effect by constructing an illusion or an ornamental detail, for example a classical porch or a dormer window. Often, it is more sensible from the buildability viewpoint to fabricate such additions either off-site or at ground level and then to lift the completed sub-assembly into position. A dormer window, for example, is complex to build in situ using traditional methods, requiring much framing up and trimming; a dormer of identical appearance can be fabricated in timber or glass reinforced polyester (grp) in the factory and then installed using a mobile crane and simple fixings.

A final comment in this section should be reserved for the effects of external forces, such as weather, upon the buildability of materials, components and sub-assemblies. Such effects can sometimes render components temporarily incompatible, for example when below freezing temperatures prevent concreting or mortar mixing, and delay and expense can result when extra materials such as additives have to be introduced to enable work to continue. Buildability is improved, therefore, if designers specify materials, components and sub-assemblies which are capable of being assembled without risk in the climatic conditions likely to prevail at the time.

**(ii) Personnel skills**   In addition to appreciating what is buildable in terms of materials, components and sub-assemblies, designers should be aware of the limits of possible construction, within differing parameters of time and cost, in relation to the site labour force. Many things have changed on site during the last twenty-five years or so, not least the skill types and levels of the operatives. Some trades have disappeared, or changed out of all recognition, other trades and sub-trades have emerged and training periods have been greatly reduced. A few of the building trades have disappeared altogether on sites where much complex fitting has to be carried out, to be replaced by those whose background lies rather in engineering. These trends have two significant characteristics: training periods have been steadily reduced, from five or six years to two or less and wage costs have risen. This has meant that, although skill levels have deteriorated in many cases, the time available to carry out the work has decreased, thereby giving a powerful impetus to buildability: a building that is easy and quick to assemble on site makes the best use of the available site labour and keeps the cost of that labour to a minimum; in other words productivity is increased. The principal changes can be summarised as follows:

(a) Increasingly, conversion takes place off-site, under the better conditions prevailing in the factory;

(b) Components and sub-assemblies are standardised as much as possible through variety reduction and repetition, enabling unit costs to be reduced and tools, plants and equipment to be used more efficiently;

(c) Site work is reduced as far as possible to the assembly of large, pre-finished components and sub-assemblies;

(d) Wherever possible, tools, plant and equipment have replaced expensive labour, echoing what has happened in manufacturing industry;

(e) Traditional trades have changed their roles, or spawned sub-trades, and new trades altogether have emerged;

(f)  There has been a sharp increase in sub-contracting, this developing in parallel with new building procurement methods, such as management contracting and 'fast-tracking'.

In general, the contrast between those assembly activities in which there is still much work to be done on site, such as concreting, and those which are performed largely off-site, is now sharper. Although off-site conversion can lead to inconveniences in delivery and handling, it can be carried out under controlled conditions, often on a production line basis, with resulting improvement in quality control. Site conditions are usually much less conducive to efficient production and high quality work, when this is complex and exposed to the weather or when continuity and a high level of interdependence between trades is necessary. Thus, when designers insist, for reasons connected with function, performance and aesthetics, upon designs which require laborious site assembly, other means must be found of saving time and money and preserving quality. Taking in situ concrete as an example, possible measures include:

- off-site production of the concrete, or tightly controlled batch-mixing and delivery to the work-place;
- highly repetitive use of formwork profiles and the maximal use of formwork components;
- rapid setting mixes, enabling the early striking of formwork;
- repetitive structural forms, enabling the use of standard or large formwork components;
- simple structural forms, enabling formwork to be simple and its use repetitive, eg as in slip shuttering;
- easy placing and compacting of concrete round reinforcement, eg by avoiding the over-tight packing of bars;
- avoidance of complex or labour-intensive finishes, eg bush-hammering or screeding;
- use of rapid casting techniques, eg strip or volumetric casting of large concrete floors;
- substitution of precast or composite systems for pure in situ work.

Another example is the fire proofing of steel frames. This activity can not be avoided, but much can be done to mitigate the problems it causes. For instance, it is always desirable and nearly always possible to avoid the 'wet' casing of steel frames. Although the casting of such casings round the columns is relatively straightforward, provided there is repetition of the formwork elements, it is a different matter constructing and supporting formwork round beams, often over a partially completed floor. The problems caused by the formwork are exacerbated by that of lifting concrete, sometimes to a high level in the building. When a crane and skip cannot be used, perhaps because floors are in place, the concrete must be pumped, usually from ground level; at high level, this can tax pump capacity. It is far better, therefore, to settle for either a dry or spray-on casing (water filled columns are also a possibility in certain circumstances). The former can be carried out by traditional trades, such as plasterers, the latter either by relatively unskilled labour or by robots: there is already on the market a machine which, overnight, will spray coat a standard steel frame entirely unaided by operatives.

**(iii) Tools, plant and equipment**   It is inevitable, in fact, that, as labour costs rise, management will seek ways of dispensing especially with high cost labout and of making that which remains more efficient. 'Tool substitution' is a way both of increasing productivity and of compensating for the loss of relatively highly skilled but expensive tradesmen. The effects upon designs of this change have been considerable, if often unrecognised in the continuing divorce of design from production; they may be categorised under two headings:

 (i) Traditional designs may no longer be assembled in traditional ways, since methods have been developed of achieving the same performance and aesthetic effects more economically;
(ii) New tools, plant and equipment have opened up new possibilities for designers: assemblies, which previously would have been prohibitively expensive, are now possible at economic cost.

Before discussing these changes, it may be helpful to give a brief summary of what is now available in the world of tools, plant and equipment, as manufacturers have responded, often with great imagination and ingenuity, to the demands placed upon them by economic forces:
– adaptations to traditional hand tools, eg ratchet and pump-action screwdrivers; these have been related to developments in fixings, such as self-drilling and 'posidrive' screws;
– more powerful and versatile versions of portable power tools, eg hammer-action masonry drills, portable circular saws;
– ranges of specialised tools, or of purpose-made adaptations to standard tools, eg floaters, trowellers, surface grinders, carborundum-tipped disc and hole cutters.

As tools become 'plant', the greatest changes that have taken place have been in site transfer handling. For economic reasons, the less time spent transferring materials, components and sub-assemblies from delivery points and storage areas to the workplace the better. In particular:
– there has been much adaptation to building purposes of plant intended originally for other uses, eg the agricultural tractor, with its almost

infinite range of attachments, the fork-lift truck, the bulldozer, the crawler-excavator;
– specialised plant has been developed, eg the tower crane fixed or railed, hoists, concrete pumps and batching plant.

Often, these developments in tools, plant and equipment have paralleled developments in the delivery and handling of materials, components and sub-assemblies. For example, bricks and blocks are delivered in sealed packs, not only to keep them clean, but also to enable them to be handled easily by fork-lift trucks, often directly onto scaffolds specially adapted by adding strong towers to serve as off-loading points; concrete is delivered in specially designed lorries, ready for placing; plumbing and heating components are supplied in knock-down kits, prepared for rapid assembly on the job.

It should be apparent, therefore, that the development of new tools for labour has made it uneconomic to continue to assemble buildings in old ways. For example, timber jointing of frames is now as efficient and durable as previously, despite being carried out in a fraction of the time using timber often of inferior quality. This is due partly to new glues and effective preservation treatment, but partly also to computer controlled woodworking machinery capable of making accurately cut joints in a few seconds. Trussed rafters, made up off-site in jigs and using nail presses and fixing plates, have displaced TDA trusses. It is no longer necessary to build timber pallets into brickwork joints, or blocks into concrete floors, to provide fixings for frames and hangers: nailable blocks, shot-firing and high strength anchors have made such interfacing components unnecessary. Further, new possibilities have opened up: modern excavators can dig, level and mound economically, making terraced or basement construction possible where once it would not have been considered. The fixing of incompatible components and sub-assemblies to each other has already been referred to, but it is worth emphasising that, because such fixing can often take place quickly and directly, the joint is simplified and the cost reduced.

Designers should not assume, however, that, because almost anything is possible, a particular design whim can be indulged without penalty and with minimal effect upon buildability. The primary purpose of tool substitution, for instance, is to speed production, especially under difficult site conditions, and to compensate for fewer operatives and lower levels of skill, not to render the impossible possible. For example, the following remain particular problems for any constructor, however sophisticated his tools, plant and equipment:
– slow, craft assembly of the primary sub-assemblies, such as loadbearing masonry walls and in situ concrete frames. No following work can begin

until the lower floors at least are complete, or until the roof has been assembled and the shell is reasonably weathertight;
- interfacing high-tolerance 'craft' components with low-tolerance 'machined' ones. Examples have already been cited (chapter 2 and appendix 1) of the tolerance incompatibility of in situ and precast concrete columns and the difficulty of interfacing blockwork and timber panel walls;
- impossible or difficult access to fixings, making 'ad-hoc' redesign or the use of special tools necessary;
- overhanging or projecting sub-assemblies, such as the upper floor illustrated in diagram 16(d). These require cantilevered or special scaffolding and pose problems for subsequent maintenance – 'buildability in use';
- cast concrete profiles which make formwork impossible to strike or to re-use;
- poor access to and circulation round the site, owing to building location, form and size;
- a multitude of foundation and service trenches, preventing the use of standard excavators and of easy access by finishing trades to buildings under construction; the specification of trenches of varying width, requiring bucket changes on the excavator;
- the need for special tools, plant and equipment, perhaps for only one or two activities during assembly;
- the requirement that heavy fittings and fixtures be supported by lightweight components and sub-assemblies, requiring extensive adaptation of the sub-assemblies;
- generally, a misplaced belief that anything can be fixed safely and permanently to anything.

A further point that designers should recognise is that the availability of more efficient assembly techniques can not compensate for components and sub-assemblies which are inherently poorly designed. For example, the joints in timber window and door frames will continue to be prone to rot, however quickly and accurately assembled they may be, as long as they rely upon traditional mortice and tenon interfaces. The solution here is either to design new joints taking full advantage of the potential of modern woodworking machinery, or to use an alternative material in which rot is impossible.

**The building: testing designs for buildability**
During the design process, it is essential for designers to consider how

buildable their designs are. To do this they should review the basic processes whereby materials are converted into components, components into sub-assemblies and sub-assemblies into the completed building, and the preparation stages, during which the materials, components and sub-assemblies will actually be converted, either off- or on-site. They should envisage how the conversions can take place and whether they can be done with a minimum of preparation, using the most widely available and best understood materials, components, and sub-assemblies. For example, the conversion and preparation for assembly into the building of a standard, timber, straight-flight stair presents no problem, whereas that for an in situ concrete one, required to fit into an odd-shaped stairwell, does:

Diagram 19(a–c) illustrates such a stair, in which apparently every sub-assembly will have to be different. This will cause complications, since two sets of formwork will be required for the flights, '$f_1$' and '$f_2$', with a third set for the landing '$l_1$'; all three sub-assemblies will have to be cast separately. An improvement would be to make both flights the same, (b), when at least the same formwork could be used for both, but the real answer is shown in (c): here, the stair is redesigned as two cranked flights, including part-landings, $l_3$ and $l_4$, joined by another part-landing $l_5$ spanning between them, the price to be paid being the realignment of the back wall.

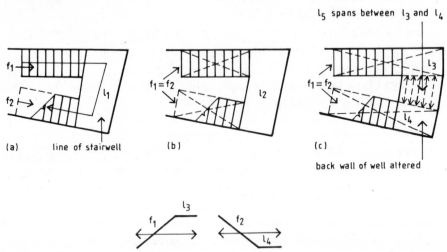

(a)  line of stairwell  (b)  (c)

$l_5$ spans between $l_3$ and $l_4$

back wall of well altered

**19**

Whereas the buildability of this design can be tested by analysis of plans, sections, elevations and details, it is necessary sometimes to explore assembly problems by means of models, or even full size mock-ups. This is done, as it would be during product maufacture under the following circumstances:

- when the final sub-assembly is complex and likely to be repeated a large number of times, either in the same or in different buildings; relatively small savings on the various materials, components and sub-assemblies and on individual assembly processes can yield large savings overall;
- when materials, components and sub-assemblies and their interfaces are unfamiliar, requiring retraining of personnel or the use of new tools, plant and equipment;
- when handling problems are likely during delivery or transfer into the building. These may require the 'knocking down' and reassembly of large sub-assemblies or the delicate handling of easily damaged items, the handling process involved having to be tested;
- when mechanical or other delicate equipment has to be tested before, and sometimes after, delivery, prior to final assembly into the building.

Although models are suitable for some of these situations, their most useful function is to explore the general layout of components and to identify likely problem areas, rather than to arrive at definitive detailed solutions. This is because they cannot simulate such factors as mass, work sizes, tolerances, real fixings and tool clearances (unless constructed full size). Combined with well designed computer modelling, however, to simulate parts which are physically unbuildable or which would be too expensive to test in actual built form, efficient testing can be carried out in this way.

Finally, it is worth emphasising as an aspect of tolerance compatibility that components and sub-assemblies which are themselves efficiently assembled may not fit when having to interface with each other at the next step up the conversion 'ladder'. Designs which are to achieve optimal buildability should be tested, therefore, for convertibility at each stage up to and including final assembly. A well known example of this is fitting kitchen units into a standard, masonry-walled kitchen:

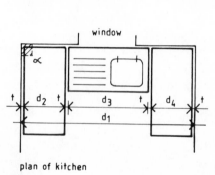

plan of kitchen

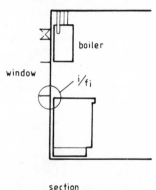

section

**20**

If '$d_1$' represents the final width of the kitchen, after the application of any linings and finishes, the units will not fit into the space if '$d_1$' is less than the sum of '$d_2$' + '$d_3$' + '$d_4$', plus a tolerance '$t$'; nor will they do so if the room, defined by angle 'alpha', is seriously out of square. The same is true of the units in section where, in addition to testing for height and position in relation to other units, there may be interfaces between units and window cills (at '$i/f_1$') and items of plumbing and heating equipment. When such layouts will be repeated many times, for example in a housing scheme or on identical floors of the same building, the construction of a mock-up has been shown to be cost effective, especially when services may be complex or tightly organised or when client approval has to be sought before production commences in earnest.

# 3 Costing buildability

Diagram 2 illustrated the general relationship between the four principal constituents of building design, function and performance, buildability, aesthetics and cost and listed the main components of each. Taking cost, the buildability factor can be studied in terms of stages of work:

initial elements:    (a)  research (including feasibility)
                          (b)  design
                          (c)  tender
                          (d)  contract
                          (e)  construction
life-cycle elements:  (f)  maintenance
                          (g)  replacement.

It is useful to think in terms of a 'buildability factor' when preparing cost appraisals for a project. The designer's success or failure in satisfying economically the requirements of tolerances, variety reduction and repetition is matched by the contractor's concern for the costs of conversion, of the labour needed for preparation and assembly and of the tools, plant and equipment needed by the labour. The buildability factor reflects the relative ease or difficulty of conversion, preparation and assembly of the building.

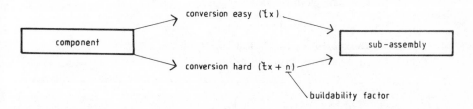

(a) **Research**   This is taken to include the briefing and feasibility phases. The brief will make no explicit reference to buildability, but will almost certainly imply that time and cost are of great importance, and it has been established that both of these factors have major buildability implications. The feasibility studies, therefore, should explore not only various ways of solving the architectural problems presented by the design programme, but also alternatives whereby buildability may be optimised. Each alternative, requiring certain combinations of materials, components and sub-assemblies, carries with it as yet unstated demands for certain types of labour, tools, plant and equipment and to get at the buildability factor, these elements must be teased out of the equation. 'Feasibility', for example, often requires a study of possible site utilisation, perhaps on expensive urban sites in the form of plot ratios, and a study designed to address all relevant factors should certainly look at possible building methods, including accesses, storage areas and the location of major fixed plant, even at this stage. Each of these factors is likely to influence the costs of the job and to reflect in the contractor's pricing.

**(b) Design**    The major parameters of buildability at the design stage have been discussed in chapter 2. When considering broad options, however, it should be remembered that each option may contain a large and sometimes disadvantageous buildability element. For example, a highly innovative building may be expensive to build, because it contains unusual materials, components and sub-assemblies, requiring new assembly techniques. On the other hand, a conservative building, containing a high proportion of repetitive elements, the interfaces between which require relatively unskilled labour and simple tools to assemble, will probably be much cheaper; the buildability factor is less critical. For example:

| Proposed design | Costs of m/c/sa, labour, plant |
|---|---|
| (1) Purpose-designed steel frame for three-storey building; varying stanchion spacings and floor heights. | £x |
| (2) Standard light steel frame for the same, dimensionally co-ordinated, with 'closed system' components | £x – 15% (say) |

Sometimes a prestigious building is requested, perhaps one in which 'corporate image' is regarded as of paramount importance. In this case, the designer may have to allow the claims of optimal buildability to be overridden by the more insistent demands of the aesthetics, but even here it is not always necessary to incur a high buildability cost. Indeed, it is positively desirable that the buildability of the hidden parts is optimised, for the higher this cost is, the less there is to spend upon those parts which are visually significant. Clients are usually interested in perceived value and efficient and economic assembly will release the cash to enable more space with higher quality finishes to be constructed. Furthermore, the worse the buildability, the longer will be the construction period, delaying the time when a client can expect to begin earning a return on his investment. This can even affect the designer and constructor: the longer a building takes to assemble, the fewer the buildings that can be designed and constructed, reducing fee income and turnover and increasing the pressure on fees and profits from that particular job. It is worth restating, therefore, the methods by which buildability costs can be reduced at the design stage:

- specify well established and understood materials, components and sub-assemblies;
- design simple and practical interfacing and fixing components;
- use standard interfaces and fixings as much as possible;
- avoid 'conversions' between materials, components and sub-assemblies which are complex, especially on site;
- avoid complex building forms;
- design for the economical use of skilled personnel during assembly;
- design for the use of widely available and versatile tools, plant and equipment;
- observe good site buildability.

**(c) Tender** Buildability can be affected at tender stage by the long-standing separation between design and construction in the building industry: because many designers are unfamiliar with what is practical on site or how easy or difficult some assembly activities are, invitations to tender can be stated in terms likely to incur increased costs. It is for such reasons that the British Property Federation, in its *Manual*,[1] calls for a split in design responsibility between architect and contractor, believing that the client will get a better return on his investment when each does what he is best at. The effect of buildability upon tender prices can be discussed under four headings: efficiency, ability to carry out the work, the degree of 'prescription' and the money available:

*(i) Efficiency* An efficient contractor will be well organised and know, usually from experience, how a particular job should be built. For example, he will know the best methods of 'conversion' and where to make the 'off/on-site' split, where to economise and take acceptable 'short cuts' and how to prepare properly for assembly, for example by selecting the most suitable formwork system or the most appropriate types of plant.

[1] British Property Federation: *Manual of the BPF System*, 1983.

Although this 'know how' is intended primarily to improve the profitability of the job, it should also be reflected in the tender price.

*(ii) Ability to carry out the work*   A job may lie well within a contractor's area of competence, but for various reasons the tender price may not be a true reflection of this ability. For example, he may be overloaded with work or be unused to the problems of building something much smaller than he is accustomed to. Alternatively, the job may be too big for him, resulting in a poor appreciation of the organisational and assembly problems associated with the work and an unduly optimistic tender price.

*(iii) Degree of prescription*   A designer may select a building system in which the assembly method is specialised and highly prescriptive, or may seek to control the quality of work by specifying how it is to be carried out. Alternatively, the implications for buildability may be poorly understood, as when inappropriate use is made of British Standards, Codes of Practice or test procedures. Unless contractors are chosen for the tender list who are familiar with the methods of assembly being proposed, high or optimistic tender prices may result. 'Performance' specifications can distort tendering as much as 'prescriptive' ones can, however: the risk with these is that contractors will be unable to propose suitable solutions to the problems being presented, or will suggest ones that depart from the aesthetic or functional objectives of the design, despite being highly buildable. The important thing, therefore, is to strike a balance between 'prescription' and 'performance' and to select contractors for tender lists, or to use tendering methods, which match the design to the contractors being asked to price it.

*(iv) Money available*   When budgets are too tight, poor buildability can result, since too many of the wrong corners may be cut, conversion may be carried out incorrectly or to low standards and low quality labour may be employed. Contractors may also be tempted to tender 'low' and then attempt to recover costs through subsequent claims.

One method of striking a fair balance between prescription and performance and between buildability and the other design criteria at tender stage is to prepare 'method statements' for those conversion and assembly activities which are critical to the function and performance or the aesthetics of the building, but to leave assembly methods for the remaining parts of the building to the contractor. The statements should be costed precisely, either in the contract documents, effectively as prime cost sums, or by the contractor himself in his tender. In this way, the designer is forced to consider in detail the assembly methods for those parts of the building which he regards as critical, whilst the contractor is free to use his particular expertise in resourcing the more familiar parts. The use of method statements is described in chapter 4.

**(d) Contract**   The effects of differing forms of building procurement upon buildability are reviewed in chapter 6. In principle, 'end-to-end' systems, such as 'lump sum' contracts, can defeat the objectives of achieving good buildability, since the contractor has not been able to make a contribution at the design stage and since the competition to achieve the lowest fixed price, based often upon inadequate data and with too little time to resource the job, has forced him to neglect this aspect. With the traditional contract, therefore, the onus is upon the design team not only to provide the fullest possible information about the job before the contract is signed, but to ensure that the building is buildable. Since these expectations can be optimistic, the cause of buildability is usually served best by adopting alternative contract forms, such as 'design/build' or 'management fee'.

Whichever form of contract is chosen, however, the costing of the job must be accurately foreseen and precisely controlled. This is difficult with the traditional Bills of Quantities and Schedules of Rates, since neither contains a suitable procedure for measuring buildability. The Bills, for example, are intended primarily as tender documents, not as practical ones describing 'work packages', although this fault is at least partially corrected in SMM 7. It should be apparent from earlier discussions that good buildability depends not only upon the content of the work, but also upon how the work is to be carried out and that both designers and contractors have a contribution to make to this understanding. A small example of how this might be achieved at tender and contract stages is shown in diagram 21:

DOCUMENT ( eg Bills )     CONTRACTOR

'Form housing in s/w floor plate for 100 x 50 stud and secure with 2 No 60 mm oval wire nails driven skew'

price: x pence per joint

(a)

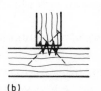

'Fix connector on stud foot and locate on floor plate ; secure with 2 No. 60 mm oval wire nails driven skew'

price:(x−5) pence per joint

(b)

**21**

The design team, proposing a buildable solution and a price for the work entailed in fixing a stud to a floor plate, have described in 'a' the conventional method for this assembly activity. The contractor, however, relying upon his particular knowledge and skills, proposes 'b', at a saving of 5 pence per joint.

**(e) Construction**   As the design moves into the construction phase, 'cost' changes from 'pricing' to 'control', with new implications for both designers and contractors. The former are concerned to control expenditure of the contract sum, with a view to achieving either an exact balance or a saving, the latter are dedicated to achieving a profit within the contract period. Both employer and contractor wish the job to go smoothly, with as few interruptions and 'extras' as possible. At this stage, however, control is very largely in the hands of the contractor since, although progress and conformity with the documentation can be monitored by the design team, it is the contractor who must spend the money to the best advantage. To do this, buildability has to be a prime consideration: at each stage of the work, from organisation, conversion, preparation and assembly through to commissioning and testing, the 'buildability factor' will be present, having an effect upon the costs of the work. For example, it is usually desirable to complete the job ahead of schedule, since this will increase turnover and may improve profits, but this will not happen if it has been necessary to pay substantial extras for the early supply of materials, components and sub-assemblies, for extra or more expensive labour or for more and more sophisticated tools, plant and equipment. The keys to profitable completion and to completion on time are more likely to be *adequate* resourcing and the efficient control of those resources and it is here that buildability becomes important: a building which can be assembled quickly and accurately renders the amount and costs of labour and equipment predictable, since absolute expenditure is limited and accurate programming is possible. There are seven areas where close attention to buildability will pay dividends:

*(i) Pre-contract phase*   A realistic tender should reflect achieveable rates of assembly. The proper preparation of the tender is therefore important, especially in such areas as formwork design, plant management, sub-contractor pricing and programming and labour type and availability.

*(ii) Contract awarded*   Negotiations between design team and contractor should take place immediately over hard-to-assemble parts of the work. Method statements, prepared as suggested in chapter 4, can help greatly in revealing these areas. Factors of particular importance include availability of materials, components and sub-assemblies, whether substitutes could be used which are cheaper and easier to assemble, at what stage conversion should take place, especially whether off- or on-site, and delivery dates and methods.

*(iii) Organising the building team*   Both head office and site teams must be organised to ensure effective cost control of the project, including

management, supervision and the work of operatives and sub-contractors. For example, lines of communication must ensure proper control and recording of deliveries, storage and on-site conversion, in addition to labour, plant and the assembly activities themselves.

*(iv) Buying*   Although materials, components and sub-assemblies must be bought in at the lowest prices consistent with agreed quality levels and delivery dates, it is essential for optimal buildability to ensure that conversion can be carried out economically and that, when substitutes are proposed, any savings will not be lost in more elaborate interfaces and fixings. It is also important in this respect for the design team not to tie the hands of the buyer by nominating or prescribing when the buildability effects can not be foreseen.

*(v) Site preparation*   Cost control must be concerned with the preparations required prior to assembly, including the numbers, type and location of temporary works, the design and type of formwork and the maintenance throughout the job of 'materials flow' into the building, from delivery and storage to final assembly.

*(iv) Assembly*   To minimise costs, assembly must be rapid and accurate. This requires the efficient deployment of a properly trained work force, using the correct tools, plant and equipment, with materials, components and sub-assemblies available at the work place when they are required. This will happen if the correct action set out in (i)–(v) has been taken.

*(vii) Testing*   Finally, testing of materials, components and sub-assemblies will usually be necessary, either prior to assembly or during the commissioning process. This can be a significant cost item, especially when installing services, and it is important that testing is carried out when the replacement of defective items can be done most economically. For example, drains should be tested before back-filling and sprinkler systems at the end of 'first-fix', before access to the pipework becomes difficult. For this reason, it is often more economical and practical to test continually as assembly proceeds, rather than once and for all at the end.

**(f) Life-cycle elements: maintenance and replacement**   Good life-cycle buildability implies lower costs for routine maintenance and for the replacement of a building's constituent materials, components and sub-assemblies as well as, ultimately, of the building itself. This aspect is dealt with in detail in chapter 8. Generally, the costs of maintenance and replacement are best controlled by establishing a hierarchy of items likely to require attention, varying from those with a short life to those which will almost certainly last the life of the building. To the former, ease of access for adjustment, servicing, dismantling and replacement are important (diagram 16(f)), whilst in the latter case delay and extensive dismantling may be tolerable. Such a hierarchy is useful, especially, when building up a likely maintenance budget for the building owner, since it will be possible to estimate the relative costs of carrying out certain items of work.

The harder it is to maintain or replace a component or sub-assembly, the better the quality of the original work must be. Efficient control of life-cycle costs, therefore, implies not only that there should be sufficient expenditure upon these critical assemblies, but that their buildability should be good since, as has been argued earlier, a failure to observe buildability principles will affect the quality of assembly. During the design process, these points should be taken into account and, as designs are developed, each component and sub-assembly should be rated for its life-cycle buildability. Diagram 22 illustrates one method of doing this:

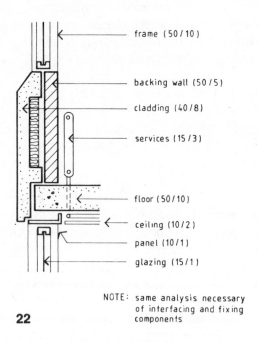

frame (50/10)

backing wall (50/5)

cladding (40/8)

services (15/3)

floor (50/10)

ceiling (10/2)

panel (10/1)

glazing (15/1)

NOTE: same analysis necessary of interfacing and fixing components

**22**

Each component in the cladding sub-assembly and its interface with the frame is rated according to two criteria: its likely life (in years) and its ease of replacement, on a rating scale of, say, 1–10. From this, it is possible to deduce relative costs based upon materials and labour constants and to change those items where the 'fit' between durability and frequency of maintenance is poor.

7

# 4 Communicating buildability

Buildability is implicit in every document prepared to explain the building, whether it be a drawing, a model or a written instruction. Even the initial sketches, which form the private means of communication between the designer and himself or his design team, contain the seeds of understanding or misunderstanding how the building will be assembled. As long as the design debate is private, this does not matter unduly – hopefully, the unbuildable options will be rejected – but should the client accept the initial ideas and then expect the building to be realised in exactly that form, trouble can arise. The well known example of this is the Sydney Opera House: a brilliant concept proved almost impossible to assemble in its original form and it was only after substantial alterations had been made that construction became a practical proposition. Even so, the high costs and long delays incurred prevented the realisation of a building with more space and better function and performance, both of which could have been improved beyond all recognition, with little sacrifice in image, had buildability been properly considered from the first 'back of an envelope' stage.

## Assembly drawings

Buildability is communicated mainly through the production drawings, often supplemented by written descriptions. Neither drawings nor descriptions, however, are concerned primarily with method of assembly: the drawings provide static, 'as built' information, giving no clue as to how the building is to be put together and the descriptions are concerned with quality control, defined in terms of amount and type of material, with references to relevant controlling standards. 'Prescriptive' information of this type, if too detailed, may obstruct rational assembly, for example by stating explictly that a sub-assembly is to be constituted of several components, some of which may be incompatible. For this reason, a properly written performance specification may sometimes be better from the buildability viewpoint, since the experienced contractor will be able to devise a sub-assembly which, whilst meeting the criteria of function, performance, aesthetics and cost, is also compatible with his knowledge and working method. Traditional production drawings, in particular, are poor at transmitting buildability information for the following reasons:

(a) they show two-dimensional sections through parts of the building and pieces of construction, chosen apparently at random in many cases, illustrating only what the construction will look like once it has been assembled; there is no sense of the dynamic process of building;

(b) they often avoid showing the important pieces of construction, for example where several components come together in three dimensions;

(c) by ignoring time, they do not show how or in what order a piece of construction is to be assembled;

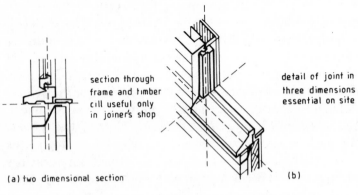

section through frame and timber cill useful only in joiner's shop

detail of joint in three dimensions essential on site

(a) two dimensional section

(b)

**23a**                    **23b**

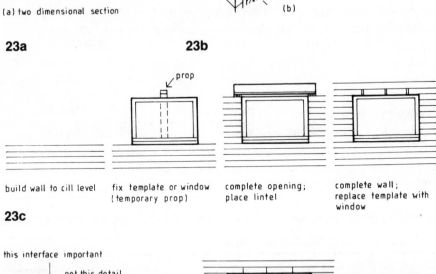

prop

build wall to cill level

fix template or window (temporary prop)

complete opening; place lintel

complete wall; replace template with window

**23c**

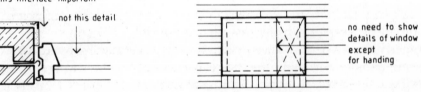

this interface important

not this detail

no need to show details of window except for handing

**23d**

(d)  they ignore the process of conversion, by which materials are changed into components and components in turn into sub-assemblies. Since much conversion takes place off-site, and all conversion is carried out at different stages prior to final assembly, drawings have to be specifically related to the degree of completeness which a building will have reached at any particular time. For example, details of a window section are required in the factory where the window is being assembled, but not at the work place, where the window is being interfaced with the wall sub-assembly.

These points are illustrated in diagram 23(a)–(d).

In the timber window shown, the critical sub-assemblies are the window itself and the wall into which it will be fixed. The window is converted off-site from timber lengths, glues and fixings and then brought on-site as a completed sub-assembly. The masonry wall, on the other hand, is converted wholly on site from several different components, bricks, blocks, mortar, dpc and so on and it is, therefore, the assembly of the wall which requires detailed assembly information to be available on site, not the window. It is not sufficient, however, merely to show the plan of the wall and the interface with the window, as in Diagram 23(d): this simply gives 'as built' data, with no clue as to how the various components in the wall are to be brought together. Diagram 24 illlustrates a better method of showing assembly details:

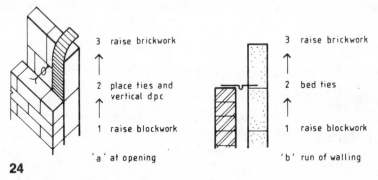

**24**

Although drawings would not be necessary for such a conventional piece of work as forming an opening in a cavity masonry wall, which lies well within the knowledge and skills of the tradesman, it will be apparent that this type of drawing is invaluable when the assembly is novel and when the best method of carrying it out has to be worked out, perhaps by designer and contractor together. Furthermore, such drawings can be useful prompts when site safety or proper performance of the final assembly are important: in diagram 24, the addition of cavity insulation batts make a considerable difference to the preferred method of assembling the wall, as

BRE has pointed out,[1] and this would have to be reflected in the detail.

## Method statements

To be fully useful, the production assembly drawings should be supplemented by some form of written instructions which describe the order in which assembly is to be carried out. These could be prepared by the designer, fully conversant with the method of assembly of his design, or by the contractor or production engineer, whose special skill and responsibility it is to ensure that a particular design can be assembled within the cost and time available for the job. If the designer passes this responsibility on to the contractor, he must still approve it to ensure that, once 'production engineered', the design conforms to his requirements for its function, performance and aesthetic appearance. The essential characteristics of a 'method statement' are that it should describe clearly the sequence of assembly of the component or sub-assembly, should illustrate the relationships between primary, secondary, interfacing and fixing components, and should cross-refer to all relevant 'quality' standards; ideally also it should be annotated for cost. Diagram 25 shows how the statement might be set out, using as an example a window cill in a masonry cavity wall:

| Sub-assembly or component | Sequence of assembly | Function and performance | Cost |
|---|---|---|---|
| $w_2$ $i/f_4$ $i/f_3$ $i/f_2$ $w_1$ $w_4$ $w_3$ $d_1$ $i/f_1$ $h_1$ | 1  raise '$w_1$' to level '$h_1$'; | | |
| | 2  add '$i/f_1$' and level; | 'brick' coursing block | £x/metre run |
| | 3  add '$i/f_2$' (dpc) | specify dpc type; ensure full lap | do |
| | 4  check height of opening '$d_1$': equals ht of '$w_2$', plus tolerance; check against no. of brick courses; | | |
| | 5  position and prop '$w_2$'; | | £x/per window |
| | 6  add '$i/f_3$' (cill); | specify cill type; ensure full mortar bed; | £x/metre run |
| | 7  add '$i/f_4$' (mastic) | specify mastic type | x pence/metre |

**25**

It is not sufficient, however, merely to describe the assembly in section: the head and jamb also require description, but, more important, so do the intersections between joints, head and cill at the corners. A complete method statement for the window/wall sub-assembly would consist, therefore, of an integration and sequencing of four drawings – of cill,

[1] Defect Action Sheet 17 (DAB 17); BRE/DOE, 1983.

jamb, head and junctions – and four listings of assembly activities, together with relevant function and performance and cost data (diagram 26):

| Sub–assembly or component | Sequence of assembly | Function and performance | Cost |
|---|---|---|---|
| (a) | (a) cill assembly (DIAG: 25) placing and propping window | as DIAG: 25 window reference | |
| (b) | (b) building up flank walls; building in dpc; | dpc reference | |
| (c) | (c) levelling walls at head; placing and bedding lintel; placing tray | lintel reference tray reference | |
| (d) | (d) lapping dpc at corners | dpc references | |
| | Window in masonry wall | | |

**26**

This composite method statement deals only with the window in the wall. The full assembly includes internal finishes, but these are not usually added until later in the assembly process and would therefore be included in another method statement dealing with wall finishes. The concept is of a set of interrelated drawings and statements which, taken together, will describe the building more or less in the order in which it will be built, as sets of coherent 'work packages'. This approach is quite different from that of trade- or materials-related descriptions. For example, Bills would be built up by collecting together sets of method statements, cross-referenced both to each other and to the production drawings. These in turn would be organised, perhaps along the lines advocated by BRE,[1] into component, assembly and location drawings, the latter being multiplied as necessary to reflect detailed assembly activities.

[1] Digest 172: 'Working drawings' and Current Paper CP 18/73: BRE (Garston), 1974.

Diagram 27 illustrates the sequence of build up, from the 'component' drawing used in the method statement to the location drawing of the completed building:

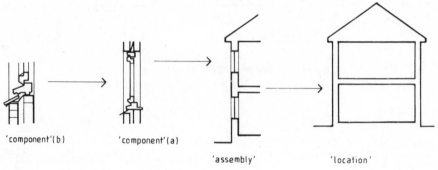

'component'(b)          'component'(a)

                                        'assembly'              'location'

**27**

It is desirable that there should not be a multiplicity of different component drawings and, wherever possible, standard assembly sequences should be used, especially at the critical on-site interfaces, so that variety reduction and repetition are achieved. For example, in diagram 27, the location drawing shows a 'unique' building made up of major sub-assemblies (walls, floors, roof, etc), which themselves may be either unique or standardised. These in turn contain components ('a' – windows), which can be used repetitively in different locations in the sub-assemblies. As long as the various detailed assemblies ('b' – cill) are standardised, however, it does not much matter how big or small the windows are, since these are assembled off-site, selected from a range, and since the walls are of masonry construction. Were the walls of framed construction, requiring variation in the frame members to accommodate different sizes of window, it would be more important for the window sizes to be standardised.

For complete clarity, drawings and method statements, together with the work packages described in the Bills, should make up interrelated sets, each set containing full function and performance data, but also allowing the assembly method and sequence to be fully understood. One way of doing this is set out below (refer to diagram 27):

| Drawing type | Purpose[1] | Assembly function |
|---|---|---|
| Location | To identify, locate and dimension parts and spaces within building and to show overall shapes by plan, elevation or section | To identify and locate primary and secondary *sub-assemblies* in relation to each other and to the building as a whole |
| Assembly | To show assembly of parts of one element, including the shape and size of those parts; to show an element at its junction with another element | To identify and locate primary and secondary *components* in relation to each other and to a particular sub-assembly |
| Component ('a') | To show shape, dimensions and composition of a component to be made away from the building or in situ | To identify and locate *interfaces* between components and adjacent components or sub-assemblies |
| Component ('b') | | To identify and locate *interfacing* and *fixing* components needed to assemble the interfaces between components or sub-assemblies |

Each drawing type is supported by a method statement, headed by the appropriate reference, describing how that particular component or sub-assembly is to be converted to the next stage up in the assembly sequence. For example, referring to diagram 25, this is a 'Component (b)' type statement describing how several differing materials and components are assembled to form a cill, enabling a window component to interface with the supporting wall sub-assembly. The next method statement, a 'Component (a)' type, would describe how the complete window fitted into the wall. The third type would describe the sequence of construction

[1] Digest 172: 'Working drawings' and Current Paper CP 18/73: BRE (Garston), 1974.

of the wall sub-assembly and the final type (location) that of assembling the various sub-assemblies ('elements' in the 'Purpose' column above) into the building. 'Component (b)' type statements would be needed, not only at the foot of this assembly hierarchy, but also wherever interfaces occurred between components, sub-assemblies and the complete building, for example between floors and walls and walls and roof. Diagram 28 illustrates, taking the example of the external wall of the house illustrated in diagram 27, how a set of method statements could be built up using this system.

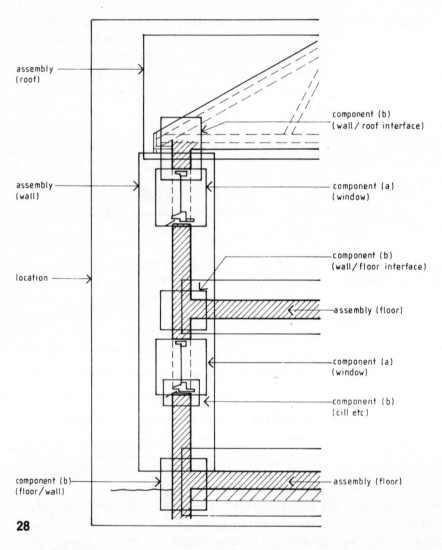

assembly (roof)

component (b) (wall / roof interface)

assembly (wall)

component (a) (window)

component (b) (wall / floor interface)

location

assembly (floor)

component (a) (window)

component (b) (cill etc)

component (b) (floor / wall)

assembly (floor)

**28**

A schedule of method statements for the external wall would consist of the following:

| Type | Assembly shown |
|------|----------------|
| Component (b) | Ground floor/wall interface |
| | Window cill, jamb, head, corners (as diagram 26) |
| | First floor/wall interface |
| | Wall/roof interface |
| Component (a) | Window assembly (may be off-site) |
| | Wall assembly (as diagram 24) |
| Assembly | Wall complete |
| | Floor(s) complete } Cross-relate to their |
| | roof complete { own sets |
| Location | Wall related to complete building |

Each of the statements would be supported, where appropriate, by drawings although, equally, the drawings for the building could contain within them the method statements. In addition, costed versions of the statements would be bound into, or form the basis of, the Bills of Quantities and Schedules of Rates.

A further point to be considered is that not all conversion takes place on site. Indeed, it has been argued that it is positively undesirable that it should do so with many standard components and sub-assemblies. Timber windows, for example, will be converted from their constituent materials in the joiner's shop, but there is no reason in principle why the same system of documentation and control should not be used as on site:

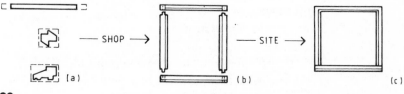

**29**

In the shop, timber is converted by adapting timber lengths (omission of material) to form the requisite profiles and necessary overall lengths (diagram 29(a)). It is then further adapted by cutting mortices and tenons (omission) (b) before being fixed together using glues and metal fixing components (c) to form the complete window. Usually, of course, when standard profiles are used and large numbers of similar windows are assembled on a production line basis, there is no need for method statements: machines, once set up, will continue to produce window sections until switched off and the workforce is familiar with the assembly sequence. But, when special profiles or non-standard window dimensions are being specified, it is important for designers to understand that the principles of buildability will apply as much in the joiner's shop as on site, and that constantly varying profiles and sizes will add significantly to assembly time and cost.

## The communications hierarchy

Buildability information is transmitted from the designer to the operative down a communications hierarchy and this process is explained in a companion volume.[1] Since the information is required for different purposes at each level in the hierarchy, it must be presented in forms acceptable and comprehensible at those levels. For example, the quantity surveyor must be able to price and control cost, the general contractor to resource the job with materials, labour and plant and the operative to understand how an unfamiliar piece of work is to be carried out. The breaking down of the production drawings into location, assembly and component types, supported by method statements, makes it possible to put together the information needed by different parties in a straight-forward way.

For example, taking the house wall illustrated in diagram 28, together with the schedule of method statements above, the documentation issued to the tradesmen might be allocated as follows:

| Type | Assembly shown | User |
| --- | --- | --- |
| Component (b) | Ground floor/wall interface | Concretor, bricklayer |
| | Window cill, jamb, head, corners | Bricklayer |
| | First floor/wall interface | Woodworker, bricklayer |
| | Wall/roof interface | Bricklayer, woodworker |
| Component (a) | Window assembly (off-site) | Joiner's shop (if purpose made) |
| | Wall assembly | Bricklayer |
| Assembly | Wall complete | Bricklayer |
| | Floor complete | Woodworker |
| | Roof complete | Woodworker |
| Location | Wall related to complete building | Bricklayer |

[1] *Quality of Site*, Ian Ferguson and Eric Mitchell, Batsford 1986.

All documents would be required by designers, quantity surveyors and contractors, both at head office and on site, by some of the trades foremen and local authority representatives and for tender and contract purposes.

## Other methods of communicating buildability

The systematic ordering of buildability information is highly suitable for computers. This is especially true of method statements which, when developed as standard solutions, can be stored in data bases and then recalled and worked on as necessary. Furthermore, the adoption of a coherent and logical form of cross-referencing enables all relevant information about a particular part of the building to be assembled quickly by the machine, checked, altered and updated, before being 'faxed' out to other consultants or to the site.

The use of scale models or full-size mock-ups has already been referred to in chapter 2. These are useful in testing the optimal order of assembly of complex interfaces, enabling method statements and drawings to be prepared, confident that the problems have been solved. They should not be neglected when considering the most appropriate means of communicating buildability.

# 5 Buildability and the contract

Although much of the material in preceding chapters may seem to be self-evident to the experienced designer and contractor, there is little recognition in the traditional contract documents of the importance of buildability in the successful execution of the works. The documents are concerned principally with matters of design quality and cost and with apportioning liability should things go wrong. Yet implicit in many of the clauses are buildability issues. For example, Clause 13 in JCT 80 (Local Authorities' edition, with Quantities), which deals with variations and provisional sums, contains no reference to the often damaging effects from the employer's point of view of changing the design, or of specifying exactly what is required only once the contract has been let and the job has been partially resourced by the contractor. The point here is that changes during the course of the works are reflections both of poor initial design and of incomplete designs and that, when these factors are present, it is either difficult or impossible to determine how assembly should be carried out. Similarly, delays caused by the Specification for work which proves difficult to construct can result in claims for extensions of time (Clause 25), another potent source of trouble. It is not always the amount of extra work which is the culprit: 'Nomination', too, is well known as a cause of dissension and delay (Clauses 35, 36). When the general contractor is required to work with sub-contractors or suppliers whom he has not been a party to selecting, he may find himself burdened not only with management problems, but with the problem of co-ordinating with the general assembly sequences incompatible sequences and unbuildable details. When it is impossible to avoid nomination, therefore, it is incumbent upon the designer, or project manager, to ensure that designs prepared by nominated sub-contractors and suppliers are buildable, that extra or special labour, tools, plant and equipment will be supplied in good time, either by the sub-contractor or by arrangement with the general contractor and that management and supervision of the work are properly co-ordinated.

It might be expected that a contractor's involvement with the design process would result in acknowledgment of the importance of buildability issues. Unfortunately, with the exception which will be addressed later, the traditional contracts make no recognition of this. For example, in JCT

80 (with Contractor's Design), Clause 8 requires that materials, goods and workmanship conform to description and that they should be available for testing or inspection, but makes no reference to the need for ease of assembly. Yet there is a clear implication in Clause 12, 'Changes in Employer's Requirements', that buildability is a relevant issue, for references are made to 'limitations of working space' and to 'execution or completion of the works in any specific order', these being regarded as possible grounds for grievance and hence, presumably, for claims by the contractor against the Employer. Even sub-Clause 12.2, whilst offering the possibility of objection by the contractor if the works are not buildable, in fact refers specifically only to 'design' and not to the effect of unbuildable design upon time and cost. Other oddities of omission in this Contract include the failure to define precisely what is meant by phrases such as 'the nature of the work to be executed' and 'the manner of its execution' (Clause 21), the doubt as to whether the failure to provide practical information might be construed as a Relevant Event in considering a claim for an extension of time (Clause 25) and the strange inclusion of 'timber used in formwork', but not 'other consumable stores' in Clauses 36 and 37. In fact, the whole matter of materials, components, sub-assemblies, labour, tools, plant and equipment needed in the preparation stages of the job, prior to assembly, are poorly dealt with, presumably because their relegation to the Preambles of the Bills is regarded as satisfactory.

Neither the Agreement for Minor Building Works, nor its Supplementary Memorandum, throw light upon the problem and it is necessary to look beyond the traditional forms and their offshoots to see whether more practical and less legalistic approaches exist.

Turning first to the ACA Form of Building Agreement (1982, 2nd edition, 1984), the relevant clauses begin with 2, 'Submission of the Contractor's drawings to the Architect'. This Clause enables the contractor to submit details of his proposed assembly method for comment and the idea contained in the Clauses that the Architect is competent to comment construcively upon buildability is given further support in Clause 5, which carries the implication that, during the 'Supervision of the Works', the Architect is competent to dismiss, or require the dismissal of, any person who 'in the opinion of the Architect' is negligent. As long as the use of the word 'negligent' refers only to the quality of work, or to the ignoring of a clear instruction, this is acceptable and time-honoured within the rules of contract administration, but if it is interpreted to mean 'the assembly is being carried out in the wrong order', a conflict of opinions could arise between the Architect and the Contractor. Moving on to Clause 8, such references as 'adjustment to obligations or restrictions to working space/working hours, access to the site or parts of the site' and 'alteration or modification of design quality or quanitity . . . the removal or bringing onto the site of any goods or materials', could be interpreted as having buildability implications, especially when supported by the rider 'on any matter connected with the Works', which invites the designer who feels concerned about some aspect of the building's production to say so. This invitation is extended further in Clause 9 in which, although the Contractor is to coordinate the design carried out by sub-contractors, it is stated that the Architect may be involved in this (although not necessarily in buildability issues). Generally, though, this document is as disappointing as the JCT series.

The Faculty of Architects and Surveyors' Building Contract follows similar lines to the others and carries the cause of buildability little further forward: the Contractor will not be held responsible for any delay caused by 'Employer's specialists'; 'Materials, workmanship and samples' are to be 'the best of their respective kinds'; variations, provisional sums and nominations hold similar terrors for the unwary and carry the same looming implications for buildability. The only glimmer of recognition occurs in Clause 12, where reference is made to the 'true intent and meaning of the drawings . . .' in relation to the 'proper and efficient execution of the Works', although the Clause as a whole is concerned with quality of workmanship rather than buildability proper.

It is not until the British Property Federation's *Manual of the BPF System* is reached that evidence emerges of a concern by the Employer for the efficient assembly of the building. The Contract Document itself, the Form of Building Agreement, based as it is on the ACA Form, is surprisingly conservative and does not reflect the much more revolutionary approach contained in the *Manual* which preceded it: there is the same failure to grasp the nettles represented by 'Employer's Liability' (Clause 7). 'Client's Representative's Instructions' (Clause 8), 'Named Sub-contractors and Suppliers' (Clause 9) and 'Employer's Licensees' (Clause 10), the only recognition of buildability problems being contained in Clause 11, 'Grounds for extensions of time', with the suggestion that valid grounds for extension might include delay or disruption by the Employer affecting the efficient assembly of the Works. The *Manual*, however, based as it is on the concept of achieving efficiency through tight control of design and cost, with full regard for the interests of the Employer, is drawn inevitably into the buildability issue. For example, since the Contractor will be contributing to the detailed design of the building, he will 'have the opportunity to ensure maximum buildability' and will have a strong incentive 'to select standard components . . . to minimise cost and problems of delivery'. There is recognition that, in the design of the foundations for instance, 'choice may have a significant effect upon the Contractor's programme and method of construction' and the Contractor is encouraged 'to propose to the Client's Representative any changes in design which will save money or time'. This concern for efficiency is carried back to the design team: 'it is important that the Design Leader and other Consultants ensure that the buildings they design can be built quickly and economically' and the specification should be written 'in a way which allows the Contractor to make the most use of his knowledge of construction methods and building components'. As the design moves forward to tender stage, it is observed that tender should include 'method statements', although these are not envisaged in the form described in chapter 4. Once the Contract is let and the job moves onto site, the Supervisor should 'record the Contractor's use of resources and the timing of activities', progress reports including 'detailed descriptions of activities begun and completed, their duration, additions to, changes in the duration of and forecast completion dates'. The Client's Representative is enjoined to 'discuss buildability and technical design with the specialist contractors' and, as the job approaches completion, the Design Leader is required to 'carry out life-cycle analyses and cost-in-use forecasts', having previously been encouraged to stress in his specification the 'importance of good access to services to assist maintenance' and to take account generally of life-cycle costing.

It is symptomatic of the cleavage between design and construction, at last and belatedly in the process of being healed, that it took a client originated document to argue forcefully for a proper recognition of the importance of buildability in the design and assembly of buildings. And it is still necessary to look to 'unconventional' contract forms, in which building procurement is seen as having as much to do with achieving a fast result at an acceptable cost as it has with observing professional niceties, to find methods which recognise that how buildings are put together is as important as the quality of their constituent parts. For example, the JCT Management Contract, intended as it is for complex projects where early completion is required and where not all the Employer's requirements are known before contract start, is likely to be a more suitable vehicle for buildability than the JCT 80 Form, since good buildability as well as efficient and flexible management is a key factor in controlling these variables. Yet, even with this contract form, the design team is distanced from the general contractor and, additionally, from the 'works' contractors, which is contrary to the requirement that integrated working from the earliest stages is necessary if designs are to be truly buildable. Some form of 'design/build' contract is preferable therefore, either one in which the contractor controls the design team, or one in which a separate, project manager-led management team controls both design team and contractors. With both these approaches, designs can be developed by the design team working with members of the building team, in the latter case additionally under strong management, committed to delivery on time and on cost and therefore to ensuring that the building is assembled efficiently and economically.

# 6 Preparation

Before assembly of the building proper can begin, a great deal of preparation has to take place. Materials, components and sub-assemblies must be identified from the drawings, specifications and Bills ordered and converted, either off- or on-site; labour types, quantities and skill levels must be made available, as must the tools, plant and equipment necessary to carry out the assembly; not least, the contracting organisations, whether general or sub, must be set up to ensure that the job can be controlled and that assembly can be carried out within the budget and time available. This last requirement is important: good buildability is not a function solely of technical performance, but also, as Savile has argued,[1] of management. For, however easy it may be to assemble a building in practice, unless management is capable of matching this ease with an equal competence, targets will not be met. It is possible to identify nine key areas about which management must be confident before assembly begins:

(1) the scope and complexity of the work must be fully understood and a realistic assessment made of the ability to carry it out to programme and to the agreed quality levels;

(2) the resources must be sufficient to complete assembly within budget and on or ahead of time;

(3) these assessment and resourcing decisions must be made when considering submitting a tender for the work; the tender should be accurate and realistic;

(4) the form of contract chosen must be appropriate for the job and for the budget and time available;

(5) both pricing and cost control procedures must be effective and reflect a concern for buildability;

(6) management, both off- and on-site, must be effective; management during assembly on site is especially important;

(7) agreed quality levels must be maintained during assembly (part of the quality assurance process);

(8) good communications must be maintained between design and building teams and especially between all members of the site team;

[1] Savile, P.: 'A practical assessment of the influence of buildability on construction sites'; MSc Thesis; UMIST, 1987.

(9) programming must be realistic, the aim being to meet, or if possible exceed, assembly deadlines.

The first part of this chapter will discuss these management issues in some detail, the second part will review specific preparations needed to ensure that efficient, buildable assembly is possible.

**(1) Scope and complexity of the work must be fully understood**   When a design team is drawing up a list of contractors for a job, or when a contractor is invited to tender, both parties must review realistically the contractor's ability to carry out the work. An organisation may be too large or too small to do the job efficiently, since overheads may be too high or the complexities beyond the competence of management and labour. The result is that the job will not be properly resourced and that site management will be unable to exercise effective control over quality and cost. To ensure that objectives are met, therefore, designers must ensure that they fully understand their designs and that the methods of assembly are practical. This level of understanding must be conveyed to the contractor, who must in turn ensure that he fully understands what is required and that he is able to assemble the building properly. He can take a positive view of this: a good contractor may see several different ways of assembling components at a particular interface, in which case he should consult with the design team and agree with it a preferred method which meets the objectives of both parties. What should *not* happen is that a job is priced without being fully understood, the contractor relying upon his native wit and experience to solve problems as they come up: that way lie claims, delays and poor morale on site. For this reason, 'fast-tracking', which by definition relies upon incomplete preparation before the job goes on site, requires decisive and excellent management to ensure that problems are solved as they arise, but within a framework of general understanding. Pitfalls can trap the unwary when it comes to 'design/ build' and 'management contracting', however, since on the one hand management may lay too heavy a hand on the design team, the 'buildability at all costs' syndrome, and on the other there may be insufficient control by the management contractors of the works contractors. As has been emphasised earlier, buildability is only one of several criteria and it is as bad to give it overriding importance as it is to neglect it. As with other things in life, a balance must be struck.

**(2) Resources must be sufficient**   There must be sufficient resources to build a job, and these include not just materials, labour and tools, but management, money and time. For example, the management team should possess the experience and expertise necessary for the job, with the ability to negotiate firmly with the design team and sub-contractors as well as to maintain good inter-personal relationships and to motivate their staff. A key need here is for effective communication (8), another is for the level of supervision on site always to be sufficient, although sensitive (6). It is management's job to maintain the flow of materials, components and sub-assemblies onto the site and to ensure that there are enough labour, tools, plant and equipment not only to assemble the building, but also to complete all the preparation necessary prior to assembly. For example, tradesmen may have to be hired to assemble special formwork or scaffolding, the ability of available plant may be insufficient for certain items of work, in which case new machines may have to be hired, leased or bought if the designs can not be changed (1), temporary roads and accesses may have to be constructed, and so on. Beyond these physical resources, management has a fundamental responsibility to ensure that the job is properly financed, that sufficient materials can be maintained in storage, that labour is hired at the right rate and is employed on the level of work appropriate to that rate, and that tools, plant and equipment are not bought when they could more cost effectively be lease or hired. Finally, time should not be saved at the expense of proper preparation which, if carried out effectively, will pay dividends when it comes to assembly.

**(3) Decisions to be made at tender stage**   It has already been empha-sised how important it is at tender stage to comprehend the scope and complexity of the work likely to be required should the bid be successful [(1) and chapter 3]. Preparation will be much easier if the job has been won on the basis of a realistic assessment of what good buildability will entail. For example, the materials, components and sub-assemblies can be measured or summarised from the tender documents, but it is essential to decide how much 'conversion' will be necessary and whether this can take place on- or off-site. If extensive on-site conversion is likely, extra workshop space may be needed or the method of site transfer handling may change. These will be added costs to the job, which might be reduced or avoided altogether if the design was altered, perhaps in some quite small respect. Or again, 'site preparation' (see below) may be complex, involving closing streets to provide storage compounds, the laying of temporary roads, the awkward positioning of the tower crane or the use of elaborate formwork and propping. Since every tenderer will be in the same position in this respect, the tender may succeed if solutions, whilst being practical, are also ingenious.

**(4) Form of contract to be appropriate**   The deficiencies of con-ventional contracts with respect to buildability have already been discussed (chapter 5). With regard to preparation, the problems derive from the separation of design from construction, resulting in the expectation that the contract documents provide a true indication of how the building should be put together, all matters of 'preparation' being contained optimistically in the Preambles to the Bills or within the contractor's assumed profit margin. That this is far from the case is demonstrated by the frequency with which provisional sums, nomination and variations occur in such conventional contracts, usually requiring changes in the preparations for assembly, often late in the day when alternative arrangements have been made. Since smooth assembly depends upon effective preparation, it is evident that assembly will be disrupted if, for example, the brick type is changed or, worse, bricks are abandoned altogether in favour of precast concrete panels. The difficulties of lump-sum contracts are compounded by the usually limited time available to the contractor to organise himself ready for work. This problem is mitigated somewhat if the time spent in tender preparation has been put to good use, for example by earmarking plant, working out a preliminary crane-management strategy and giving advance warning to sub-contractors and suppliers, but it is still a very short time in which to organise formwork supplies and scaffolding, say, to divert or obtain new plant and to hire new personnel. Although a well-organised contractor, with computerised efficiency, may manage the problem easily, even he could do a great deal better given more time and earlier access to the design information. It is for this reason that newer contract forms are more suitable if optimal buildability is to be achieved and preparation time put to good use. For example, a 'design/build' contract should give the building team such early access to the designer's intentions, that not only can it influence the design team away from hard-to-build solutions, but also make possible the earliest provision for labour, tools, plant and equipment likely to be needed. A project manager-led, management fee contract, on the other hand, by bringing design and building teams under strong, centralised management, should enable differences to be settled and effective preparation to be carried out in close relationship to the assembly process.

**(5) Pricing and cost control procedures must be effective**   At tender stage it is essential that pricing takes fully into account the likely costs of preparation, but this care must be exercised up to the point where the contract has been secured and orders have been placed for materials, components, sub-assemblies, labour, tools, plant and equipment. Only then will the full costs of the job become apparent. It is essential that these include proper assessments of all work needed prior to assembly, including the labour and special equipment which may be ncessary to assemble and dismantle temporary works, the costs of phasing the work so that plant can be used efficiently and the provision of suitably equipped storage and workshop facilities. Much preparatory work is complex and expensive. To take an historical example, most of the cost and ingenuity expended upon erecting the high vaults in a Gothic cathedral were centred on the timber scaffolding and formwork; the laying of the stone, once cut to size and shape, was relatively straightforward. Similarly today, a correct assessment of the best method of casting an in situ concrete floor slab is important if formwork costs are to be minimised.

Once the job has been accurately priced, the next essential is to ensure that costs, including those for preparation, are controlled as work proceeds. To maintain control, preparatory work on such items as formwork should include proper inventories, with the costs of storage, handling, erection, dismantling and replacement calculated over the period of use. It is here that good buildability can help: repetition of formwork components, components that are simple and easy to erect and durable components will speed work and reduce expense. Similar control must be exercised over sub-contractors such as scaffolders, since scaffolding and staging should only be kept on site for minimal time; it is for this reason that design can have a significant effect upon the costs of preparation, since if scaffolding can be 'designed out' or simplified, unproductive work can be reduced. A key element in site control of costs at preparation stage is knowing what is on site, where it is, what it is doing, how often it will have to be repaired or replaced and how soon it can be got off-site. It is essential, therefore, that accurate records are kept – and here the site computer can help – and regularly updated, so that, for example, crane down-time can be allowed for, utilisation maximised and likely date off-site known with some precision.

**(6) Management must be effective** Clear objectives for the project must be agreed by all members of the design and building teams, and especially by the site team, before work starts, so that personnel know what they are doing and that nothing happens by accident. A good, buildable design is easier to understand and programme than one which is hard to assemble and management's tasks will therefore be easier. The principal objectives of any project are to assemble the building on time, on cost to the agreed quality levels. Management's strategy for achieving these objectives are firstly, to agree the design at the earliest possible stage, to set up a project planning team sufficiently experienced and knowledgeable to handle the work and, thirdly, to agree sets of procedures which will ensure that the job is properly controlled. In practice this means selecting the right staff for key positions, briefing personnel clearly at all stages, establishing good communications (8), motivating properly, controlling costs and running the job to a realistic but challenging programme (9). Buildability, as Savile[1] has pointed out, is as much to do with effective management as it is with technical performance and nowhere is this more true than at the preparation stage of a project.

**(7) Agreed quality levels must be maintained**   Although buildability is important, it must not be a substitute for 'quality'. Standards in function, performance and aesthetics must be maintained, and the striking of a fair balance between 'quality' and buildability is a key role of management. In particular, this is a problem for the quality assurance team who, before assembly begins, must address themselves to a number of key questions. For example, are the quality standards set for the materials, components and sub-assemblies the correct ones, are materials, components and sub-assemblies available which meet those standards, can conversion take place on-site without standards being compromised, are the operatives capable of carrying out assembly at the appropriate quality levels and will the quality of the completed building be at least equal to that of individual components and sub-assemblies? It is important to appreciate that an effective quality assurance system is as much concerned with efficiency in assembly as with the meeting of Codes of Practice and British Standard Specifications, and the testing of a design for good buildability is an important part of the team's work.

**(8) Maintaining good communications**   Several studies have emphasised the importance of communication in ensuring both that a design is buildable and that all relevant information is made available to the site staff during the course of the work. Because much detailing of buildings is carried out by junior staff, solutions proposed can sometimes be incorrect and with practical problems of assembly ignored, resulting in late changes in design and the need for new preparatory works. Once the design arrives on site 'valuable time is wasted by contractors in searching for the appropriate drawings when clearer details and better referencing of drawings could lead to quicker assembly'.[2] This view is confirmed by NEDO,[3] who state that 'design must be resolved in every detail before work starts, so that staff know what they are doing and that nothing happens "by accident"'. The importance of providing clear, accurate information to enable assembly to proceed smoothly has already been emphasised (chapter 4), but such information carries with it implications for the preparation stages and management must ensure that requirements

---

[1] Savile, P.: 'A practical assessment of the influence of buildability on construction sites'; MSc thesis; UMIST, 1987.
[2] ibid.
[3] 'Achieving quality on building sites': Bg. Econ. Dev. Committee; NEDO, London, 1987.

for such matters as scaffolding and formwork are fully understood by the site team. One method of doing this is to involve the site supervisory staff, and especially the site manager, in the planning stages of the job, drawing upon their practical and up-to-date experience and ensure their commitment to the programme and the project's objectives. By bringing site staff into contact with their opposite numbers in head office early on, communications during the course of the work should be improved: there is a 'face' as well as a voice at the other end of the telephone. It is during these preparatory sessions that buildability issues should be discussed, for example regarding formwork assembly, temporary access and the location of fixed plant. It is also the time for setting up the communication links between head office and site that will be crucial to the smooth running of the job, especially when things go wrong. The basic communication system is shown in diagram 30:

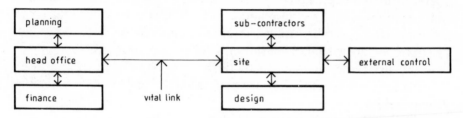

**30**

It should be noted that, once the job goes on site, although the site becomes the focus and clearing house for day-to-day management and job control, close links must be maintained with head office, which usually retains responsibility for such matters as staffing, estimating and buying, as well as the normal line management activities. To maintain these links, personal contact is as essential as the telephone and the computer and for this reason the contracts manager has a key role. It is he who will provide a backup to the site manager and ensure that head office is kept fully informed about progress, but he is also well placed to ensure that the information flow to the site is maintained, that errors are corrected quickly and that disputes involving personnel are resolved amicably. Of particular value in ensuring the two-way flow of production and financial information is the setting up of a contract dossier, the purpose of which is to record against date and time all key decisions and requirements, together with their financial implications. Allied to a computerised recording system, this can become a powerful management tool, not least in the resolving of buildability problems. For example, against each assembly activity can be recorded the preparation needed, including such items as formwork type and quantity, labour and plant, as well as the type and quantity of the materials and components themselves, with their delivery dates, storage and handling requirements and method of conversion. By updating this information regularly, it should be possible to foresee possible delays, labour and plant overloads and cash flow, thereby enabling corrective action to be taken in good time. Given modern communication and information systems, control of the job from anywhere within the organisation is possible, consistent with the need to maintain personal contact, and for this reason, on larger jobs, line management can be as effectively based on site as in head office. This in turn suggests the development of new roles and methods of job running, for example with the 'contracts' becoming the 'project' manager and the site agent becoming the 'site manager' proper, each equipped with more powerful tools and wider responsibilities than heretofore.

**(9) Programming must be realistic but challenging**   Programming by whatever method depends upon assessments of the time needed to carry out assembly activities, and buildability is therefore a key factor in ensuring that assembly times are minimised. At preparation stage, programme review should consider the following questions:
- which are the key assembly activities?
- which assembly activities depend crucially upon other assembly activities?
- which assembly activities can run concurrently?
- which assembly activities can be omitted or combined?
- can certain assembly activities be 'designed out'?
- is extra preparation needed for certain assembly activities? If so, how much delay will this entail?

For example, the frame of a framed building is essential, since the rest of the building depends upon it, but the type of frame might be laborious to assemble and time would be saved if it was changed. Since such a fundamental alteration would probably be impossible at this stage – it is the job of the design team to address this kind of problem – the review moves on to consider various other ways of saving time, for example by using repetitive formwork systems or by dry casing steelwork. Or again, space on site may be so constricted that the assembly has to be phased, with temporary works and fixed plant partially or wholly dismantled and re-erected in new positions, thereby incurring delay. It is apparent, therefore, that it is never too early to begin programming, especially when rapid completion is a condition of the contract, and even during the design phase the designer should have in mind not only how and in what order his building is to be put together, but also how long the process is likely to take. It is worth emphasising, therefore, that the better understood the assembly method is, the more accurate the programme can be and the greater the likelihood of it being followed. It is also vital that the drawings and other documents communicate the design intention clearly, so that the building can be properly understood and a programme prepared which is realistic and attainable.

## Preparation: the principles

Before proceeding to consider some of the practical issues affecting buildability at the preparation stage, it is worth restating the principles of the discipline expounded in chapter 1 and demonstrating how they apply to preparation.

It was explained that, before materials could be converted to components, or components to sub-assemblies, they usually had to be adapted in some way, by omission or addition of material, by changes in specification or by the interposing of interfacing and fixing components. This work of adaptation, or conversion, has to take place before assembly during the preparation stage, either off- or on-site. But, whereas off-site conversion takes place in various factories and workshops scattered around the country, on-site conversion must be carefully organised to dovetail with the physical capabilities of the site, with its workforce and equipment and with the demands of the programme. Diagram 31 sets out the various stages at which conversion can take place as materials, components and sub-assemblies 'flow' across the site:

Off-site conversion takes place on receipt of order, unless items are already available from stock. Items are then delivered, handled to storage and, when needed, are handled across the site to the workplace before being assembled into the building. But, whereas some items are ready for assembly directly into the building without any further work being necesary, others may need a good deal of work doing to them before final assembly is possible. For example, roof trusses and timber stair flights would follow sequence (a), since they would be ordered somewhat ahead of programme to ensure availability and since the costs of storage would not be excessive. On the other hand, concrete materials and joinery timber would be delivered as bulk items (b), conversion to components and sub-assemblies taking place after a period in storage and before they were handled across site to the building. Plastering and mortar materials would be converted at the workplace (c), and 'knock-down' items, such as plant room equipment and door-sets, would effectively be converted twice, once during assembly in the factory and again before final assembly into the building (d). Finally, some items would be ready for immediate assembly and their bulk, complexity and cost would dictate delivery direct from the factory to the workplace, with any intermediate conversion being minimised (e). The diagram is, of course, simplified to make the principle

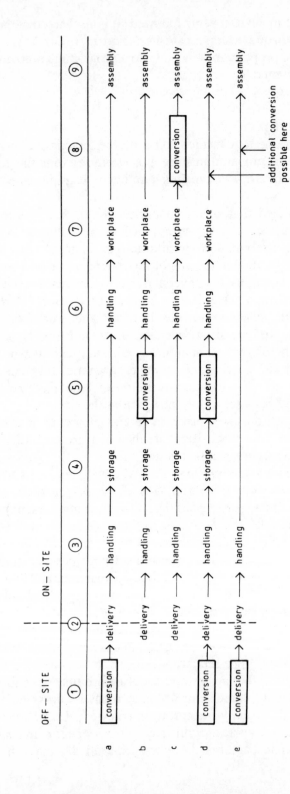

31

clear; in practice, conversion is often not as straightforward, concrete for example, containing materials (sand, water, aggregates) and one 'component' (cement), which has had to be converted in the factory.

Buildability during the preparation phase is concerned with operating upon the building process illustrated in diagram 31 and with deciding which materials, components and sub-assemblies should pass through which stages (1–9) and whether stages can be shortened or eliminated. For example, delivery of a sub-assembly direct to the workplace on the delivery vehicle cuts out intermediate handling and storage, stages 4 to 8, but removes the flexibility which is possible when items are retained in storage: storage acts as a 'buffer' in the system, not available when items have to be fixed immediately. On the other hand, large numbers of small items, requiring not only handling and storage but conversion at one or more stages before they can be assembled into the building, soak up both time and labour and complicate programming. Skilful design and organisation for buildability therefore seeks to achieve the following objectives during this phase of the work:
- the elimination of stages in the building process, by converting off-site where possible, and by the substitution of direct assembly for handling, storage and conversion on site;
- the speeding up of each stage, by tight programming and by applying the principles of variety reduction and repetition;
- the correct identification of which materials, components and sub-assemblies must pass through which stages;
- the relating of these needs to the resources of labour, tools, plant and equipment available to carry out the work.

For example, steelwork erection is speeded and simplified if stanchions and beams are delivered with plates and cleats already attached and with bolt holes pre-drilled: interfacing components are needed, but do not exist as separate items for the site to worry about. Or again, concrete is usually better converted off-site and supplied direct to the workplace, which not only eliminates the storage and handling of materials and components but also make changes in concrete specifications relatively easy. Timber components may be converted in a number of ways and at different stages and here programming and labour resources must dictate the best course: should door frames be knocked up on site or supplied as door-sets? How long will delivery of kitchen units take? Can skirtings be eliminated altogether? Will a slow but versatile item of plant be better than a quicker but more specialised one? Will the rate agreed for joiners and plasterers buy the skill level needed to assemble a complicated staircase? With these and similar questions in mind, it is possible now to look in more detail at what in practice must be done during the preparation phase of the project.

**Preparation: the practice**
In addition to the conversion of materials, components and sub-assemblies
ready for assembly into the building, the physical environment of the site
must be such as to facilitate the assembly process. The creation of a
suitable environment depends upon the provision of the labour, tools,
plant and equipment necessary to receive the materials, components and
sub-assemblies onto the site, to handle them, store them, deliver them to
the workplace and generally to assist their assembly into the building. The
following are the main constituent parts of the site environment:
– temporary works including:
  (a) accesses and temporary roads
  (b) offices, facilities for personnel
  (c) storage areas and workshops
  (d) temporary services; fuel points
  (e) scaffolding and staging
  (f) formwork and propping
  (g) shoring, planking and strutting
– labour, tools, plant and equipment needed to erect, maintain and
  dismantle the temporary works;
– labour, tools, plant and equipment needed to maintain the flow of
  materials, components and sub-assemblies into the growing building,
  prior to actual assembly.

*Temporary works*
*(a) Accesses and temporary roads*   It is not always possible or desirable to
use the permanent accesses to the building during the assembly process.
They can be damaged by heavy site traffic and delivery vehicles,
obstructed by groundworks and render efficient through-circulation of
heavy vehicles impossible. It may be impossible to deliver bulky items
using them (chapter 2, diagram 15) and sub-contractors may need 'private'
accesses to their own compounds and stores. For these reasons, it is usual
on many sites to provide two or more site access points for vehicles and to
contrive through routes, as illustrated in diagram 32:

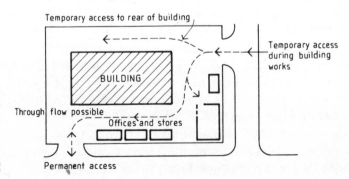

**32**   Permanent access

Temporary roads, although saving wear and tear on permanent bases, are expensive and should be avoided if possible, but they are often unavoidable if plant needed for assembly must be brought close to buildings, if carting to spoil heaps or delivery to otherwise inaccessible parts of the site is necessary or if bulky and heavy items must be delivered to the workplace. Intelligent planning, allied to a building design which has considered site buildability, can reduce the need for them considerably. For example, storage compounds and spoil heaps can be relocated near to permanent roads, plant can be used which is not dependent on a consolidated surface, the permanent road bases can be used for lighter and less damaging vehicles and 'portable road systems' quick to lay and recover, can serve where ground conditions and vehicle axle loadings permit. The essential consideration is, will the trade-off between cost and convenience be justified in terms of improved 'flow' onto and through the site?

*(b) Offices, facilities for personnel*   The efficiency of the site and the well-being of the workforce depend upon control and supervision of all the site's activities and upon proper accommodation and facilities. Entry to and exit from the site will require control points, for example, for checking deliveries and directing vehicles to the correct off-loading points as well as for maintaining security. Office locations should, where possible, ensure that visual control of entry, exit and circulation routes, as well as of the building itself, can be maintained. This is not just for reasons of control: good management and efficient performance depend upon keeping a balance between direction and trust and if personnel feel that management is fully aware of what is going on, the quality of work on site is likely to improve. Similarly, a concern for people's comfort and safety is bound to yield dividends. In buildability terms, the offices are the nerve centres of the site, where information is received, processed and issued and where the key tactical decisions affecting programmes and cost control are made. For these reasons, the offices should be accessible equally from the street outside and the site itself, so that visitors can be received, meetings set up with minimal delay and the least possible time lost in moving between offices and workplaces.

*(c) Storage areas and workshops*   After delivery vehicles have passed through the entry check-points, they proceed either to a storage area or to the building. Their routes to these areas should therefore be direct and require the minimum of manoeuvring or of travel through mud or poorly consolidated ground. During off-loading, vehicles should not obstruct the circulation routes, a problem hard to avoid on 'tight' sites or when, for example, frequent deliveries of ready-mixed concrete are being made. The

basic pattern of circulation routes on a busy site is illustrated in diagram 33:

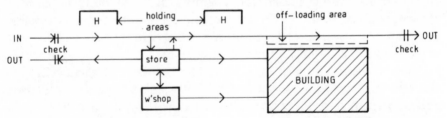

**33**

After entering the site, vehicles proceed either to the storage area or to the building, where they off-load. They then either return to the entry point, if there is only one point, or continue to the secondary or other exit points. To maintain circulation at busy times, it is desirable to provide both holding and off-loading areas ('H' in the diagram), although this luxury can not often be afforded. It will be noted that there are close, two-way links between the storage area, workshops and the building, since conversion of some materials and components may take place either after a period in storage or in the building itself (diagram 31); after conversion, too, the newly assembled components may have to be returned to store until they are required.

Site circulation and storage arrangements can be complicated by the need to provide for sub-contractors, who may require their own bases within the site. These can include storage, workshop and domestic facilities, more or less self-contained and either 'permanent', when work will be taking place during a large part of the contract period, or temporary, when operatives may share some of the general contractor's accommodation.

Since buildability is affected by the flow of materials, components and sub-assemblies through the site, the location and method of their storage is important. Storage is usually located in a secure compound for those items which are likely to be easily damaged, which are prone to vandalism or theft, which will require conversion in a nearby workshop or which will not be required in the building for some time. Other items will be off-loaded at various points on the site, near to the work places, or simply adjacent to the delivery vehicles' route, for onward handling by other plant. Storage must take into account the sensitivities of different materials to their storage environments and to the risk of accidental damage. For example, bricks can be damaged by careless off-loading, by stacking on soft ground and by storing too close to vehicle routes, whereas timber and joinery components are liable to become wet if left unprotected from the weather and require drying out before they can be assembled into the building. Some items, for example plasterboards and dry-wall partitions, are best stored in the building itself, others, such as cement and paints, in dry, ventilated sheds. In each case, plant may be needed to off-load and handle to store and this can cause difficulty and incur expense if routes between delivery point and store are poor or require special equipment. For example, fork-lifts need reasonably level ground, unbroken by waste or excavation, whilst cranes may have to off-load onto scaffolding towers before items can be moved into the building. Various storage conditions are illustrated in diagram 34:

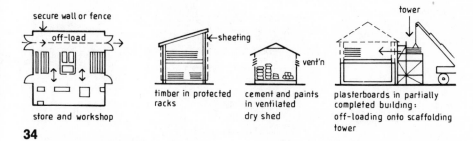

**34**

Storage areas should be secure, but it should be possible both to commit items to storage and to extract them ready for conversion or onward handling with minimal difficulty or delay.

*(d) Temporary services and fuel points* Effective preparation depends upon the provision of electrical, water and drainage services on site, located in the appropriate positions, that is adjacent to offices, workshops and fixed plant as well as in the building. In addition, fuel and water will be required for mobile plant, plus gases for welding and compressed air. For example, during the concreting of an in situ floor slab in a medium size building, the following services will be needed:

| Task | Plant used | Services/fuels |
|------|------------|----------------|
| Form work assembly | Crane | Electricity |
| | Power/hand tools | Electricity/ Compressed air |
| Placing concrete | Crane | Electricity |
| | Pump | Diesel – not always required |
| | Vibrator | Petrol/Mixture |
| | Tamper (double-beam) | Petrol/Mixture/ Compressed air |
| Finishing concrete | Floater; troweller | Petrol/Mixture |
| | Grinder | Petrol/Mixture |

These power and fuel supplies must be laid on in time for work to begin and located so that no undue delay is caused in refuelling or breakdown. Their choice is also important: noisy plant may not be permissible on urban sites, for example, and, following buildability principles, the variety of different types of power supply or fuel should be reduced to a minimum. Diagram 35 illustrates a typical distribution of services on a site of moderate complexity.

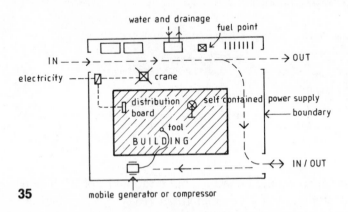

**35**

*(e) Scaffolding and staging*   These are essential items of equipment on all construction sites, providing safe access to the works during both assembly and preparation stages as well as off-loading points for materials, components and sub-assemblies adjacent to the workplace. Until recently, scaffolding was exclusively either of the putlog or independent types, but most is now independent or 'system' in design, since these are quicker to assemble and do not require making good to the building face after striking. Staging, either fixed or mobile, is exclusively 'system' in design and is quickly demountable; it is used where particular items of work require less than full scaffolding, in confined spaces and where rapid movement from one location to the other is necessary. Special scaffolding, for example of the 'hanging' type, is also available.

Buildability is adversely affected by complex building forms and the consequent need for complex scaffolding. Not only will such scaffolding take longer to erect, it will also probably have to be dismantled and re-erected during the course of some of the work, especially when the assembly sequence has been poorly considered. Similarly, it may be necessary to dismantle and re-erect internal staging, for example where spaces have been sub-divided by internal partitions. The buildability characteristics of the different systems vary:

*Putlog:*     Obsolescent: relatively poor buildability owing to the need to make good to the fabric after dismantling; not versatile, since depends upon building for support; many small components add to time and cost of erection and dismantling.

*Independent:*     Relatively poor buildability, since must be tied back to building through openings, thereby delaying filling openings until scaffolding struck; not versatile, since supported by building, and many small components.

*System:*     Inherently stable, with minimal tying back needed; less flexible, owing to boxed sections, but fewer separate components necessary; quick to erect, but height limited.

*Special:*     Necessitated by special or complicated assembly methods and building forms, such as timber frame, precast panel, 'no fines', chimney construction and overhangs; intrinsically expensive, but may be justified if use of full height scaffolding can be avoided.

Sometimes scaffolding can be dispensed with altogether, for example when fixing precast panel cladding units from inside the building, and from the buildability aspect this is desirable, since preparation is much simplified. Failing this, however, designers should recognise that a complex building profile can be as much of a headache to the contractor as it is a source of profit to the specialist scaffolding erector. Diagram 36 (i–iv) illustrates some of the situations to avoid:

(i) *'Lean-to' design*   scaffolding is raised to assemble the main wall 'A', but must be dismantled and partially re-erected to assemble the 'lean-to' wall 'B'.

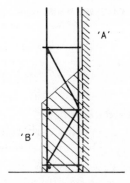

(ii) *Overhangs or projecting elements*  scaffolding must be designed either to double-depth on plan, or to cantilever once overhang is reached.

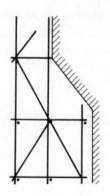

(iii) *Rendered upper storey*  since rendering takes place late in the assembly sequence, striking the scaffolding must be delayed. This interferes with work at ground level and adds to cost, since scaffolding must be retained for an uneconomical period.

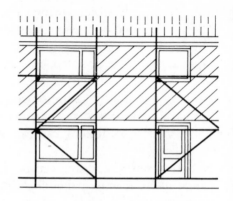

(iv) *Scaffolding between adjacent buildings*  effectively obstructs access between the buildings, making diversions or even temporary accesses necessary.

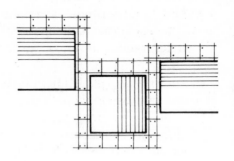

(v) *Partitions and staging*  partitions erected early in the job, necessary when they are loadbearing, make use of internal staging difficult. Non-loadbearing partition assembly must await dismantling of staging.

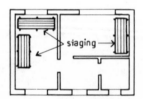

(vi) *Cladding* panels which must be fixed externally may require the retention of scaffolding, but the scaffolding can obstruct the handling of the panels
(See Application Study 1).

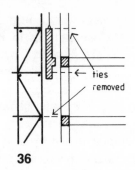

← ties removed

**36**

**(f) Formwork and propping** With all forms of in situ concrete construction, formwork is a major consideration at the preparation stage, requiring sometimes as much design as the permanent structure. Yet it is frequently neglected by building designers, responsibility being passed to formwork engineers, who must contrive suitable moulds based upon their interpretations of the architect's and structural engineer's requirements. When designs are straightforward, this method of working is acceptable, but when they are complex or non-repetitive, it is essential that the original designers are familiar with formwork practice and apply buildability principles to it. Indeed, formwork design will reflect the design of the building itself closely, a complex and hard to assemble building finding its echo in the formwork. Thus the principles of variety reduction, repetition and conversion and a respect for tolerances and an optimal assembly sequence should be applied with rigour. For example, the use of standard components is desirable, as is the avoidance of complex support and spanning systems, which although modular and designed to meet every conceivable need, complicate inventories, storage and maintenance. Intricate profiles or superfine finishes require precision in assembly, careful finishing of internal surfaces and care in striking, calling for specially skilled labour and extra time, whereas undercut profiles may be impossible to strike without causing damage to the concrete.

**Formwork** may be assembled from timber sheets or boards, or steel sheets, sometimes with linings such as melamine to give a smooth surface once the forms are struck. The surfaces are boxed, then framed to give strength and to prevent movement during concrete placing, and may be supported above ground or at upper floor levels by various systems of joists and props. It follows that sheets should be modular wherever possible, with moulds formed from sub-divisions of standard sheet sizes, and used repetitively up to the end of their useful lives. With steel sheets, converted specially for the job or used for slip-shuttering, maximal repetition is even more important. Repetition is relatively easy to achieve with troughed or 'waffle' floor designs, since the modular units are small and, in the average wide span floor, used a large number of times. Care should be taken, nevertheless, to ensure that the floor contains full 'bays' and that the grp moulds themselves are standardised, if possible throughout the building. The buildability criteria for formwork may be summarised as follows:

- minimal variety and maximal repetition;
- efficient conversion of materials to formwork components;
- maximal use of components up to the end of their useful lives;
- appropriate choice of materials: timber, steel, plastics;
- design to permit rapid erection and striking;
- design to permit straightforward setting out, plumbing, aligning;
- no awkward internal projections;
- enough space within moulds for reinforcement, concrete and vibrators;
- finishes not to be better than necessary for location in building;
- design to allow for obstruction of working space by support systems;
- support systtems to be versatile and with fewest number of separate components.

Diagram 37 (i-v) illustrates some of these points:

(i) Mould dimensions should be standardised and modular as far as possible, to minimise variety and maximise repetition; 'a' shows the kind of design to avoid.

(ii) Differing systems on the same job require different materials, components, sub-assemblies, assembly methods, and complicate control, storage and handling.

(iii) Moulds with inserts or with complex sections are time-consuming to assemble, expensive and sometimes difficult to support firmly.

(iv) Undercut forms are impossible to strike.

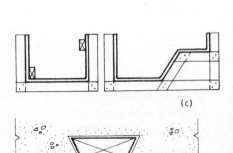

(v) Curved forms, especially if
radii of curvature alter, are
difficult to assemble.

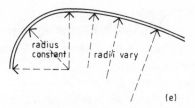

**37**

(e)

It should be emphasised that, whilst work on the formwork is proceeding in one part of the building, operatives and plant will be busy with the assembly sequences elsewhere, since preparation and assembly stages must frequently take place in parallel as well as sequentially. This affects the number of different trades on the job at any one time and their ease of access to the workplaces, since props and shores can occupy much of the floor space near to formwork. It also affects plant management, in that the crane will sometimes have to handle simultaneously formwork components and components required for the building proper, such as concrete.

**Propping**   is defined as that system of temporary supports needed to maintain components and sub-assemblies accurately in position, either whilst they gain working strength or whilst other work on them is completed. An example of the former is in situ concrete assembly, of the latter the holding in plumb and alignment of precast panels or window frames. Props should be standardised but versatile (adjustable), but regardless of how effective they are, they can cause obstruction and delay. For example, heavy loadings will require many props, often with cross-bracing, and it may be necessary to retain props in position for quite long periods whilst concrete gains its full working strength. It is desirable, therefore, to minimise the need for props, for example by using joists and floor-centres spanning between walls or major support points, or by specifying rapid-setting mixes enabling striking to be carried out sooner. The major contribution to minimal propping, however, can often be made by the designer who, by considering the problem from the outset, may be able either to 'design it out' or to ensure that structures are self-supporting during final assembly.

**(g) Shoring, planking and strutting**   It is necessary to support and prevent the collapse of structures and excavations during the assembly process, and the erection of shores and trench linings is often a necessary part of the preparation stage of a job. Shoring of buildings adjacent to the site may be required until the new building or a rebuilt wall has been constructed and these often massive assemblies can cause considerable obstruction to operatives and plant. For this reason, work should be planned to take assembly sequence and plant location and movement into account. Planking and strutting of excavations varies from the sheet piling and cofferdams needed to retain earth and water in deep basements to simple trench lining. Buildability is assisted either if the retaining system becomes part of the final structure, as when sheet or interlocking piles are used, or if proprietary systems are introduced which enable work to proceed rapidly. For example, 'knock in' linings are simple to use and safe, since the excavator drives the linings in before operatives enter the trench, whilst types which rely upon expanding struts are able to withstand high pressures and reduce obstruction in the trench to a minimum. As with formwork and propping, the designer can contribute to buildability by 'designing out' the need for elaborate systems, for example by specifying piles or rafts instead of strip foundations in difficult soils or by the alternative basement retaining wall methods referred to earlier.

## Labour, tools, plant and equipment needed to erect, maintain and dismantle the temporary works

(a) **Labour**   Efficiency dictates that the labour force retained on a job is sufficient in number, type and quality, to enable the work to be carried out on programme and within budget. The erection, maintenance and dismantling of the temporary works do not contribute directly to the assembly of the building, but are essential to enable the assembly to be carried out. For this reason, the labour content at this stage of the work should be minimised. There are various ways of doing this, easily deduced by the reader from earlier chapters:

– temporary works can be 'designed out' in the manner already described. For example, precast concrete or composite flooring systems can be substituted for in situ concrete floors;
– the temporary works can be rationalised according to buildability principles, their variety being reduced, repetition of standard units increased and erection and dismantling simplified;
– simpler erection and assembly enables less labour and less expert labour to be employed;
– the same labour can be used for the temporary works as for assembly of the building, thereby making deployment of labour easier, since more flexible;
– specialised, especially sub-contract, labour can be avoided wherever possible.

Proper maintenance of the temporary works is important. A prime requirement is safety, since building sites are dangerous places and operatives will not work confidently and efficiently when safety has been neglected. Once safety has been attended to, however, the works must be maintained in good condition. For example, scaffolding must be both secure and raised to the correct level in good time for assembly to begin, whilst formwork must be checked carefully for alignment and firmness, to ensure that it will not move as concrete is being placed. It should be possible to assemble and dismantle components easily and to this end cleanliness and the lubrication of bolts, screws and other fixings are important.

**(b) Tools and plant** Special tools and plant may be needed for the erection and dismantling of the temporary works, varying between the scaffolder's podger to special jacks, and manipulative tools for formwork, caissons and so on. Although the cost of many of these items may be insignificant, non-availability may cause delay or incorrect assembly. It is important, also, to apply the same principles to tools and plant as to labour: fewest tools and fewest number of special tools as possible, use of tools which will speed up the work significantly and the same tools and plant as are required for the assembly of the building. It should be remembered, however, that economies of this sort should not be achieved at the expense of 'overload': a crane fully engaged in handling sub-assemblies will not be available to lift and place formwork, hence duplication or substitution may sometimes be justified, for example by providing concrete pumps or mobile cranes.

**Labour, tools, plant and equipment needed to maintain the flow of materials, components and sub-assemblies into the growing building, prior to actual assembly**

**(a) Labour** For assembly of the building to take place smoothly and without interruption, those carrying out the work should be able to rely on all the materials, components, sub-assemblies, tools, plant and equipment which they need being available to them at the workplace at the right time. This ideal can rarely if ever be achieved, but management's responsibility is to ensure that it is at least striven for conscientiously. Good buildability at the point of assembly depends upon proper preparation, a function of all the factors already discussed, but specifically upon:
- clear understanding of what is required, affecting the design intention and its supporting documentation;
- unimpeded and safe access to the building at the point of assembly;
- availability of all necessary materials, components and sub-assemblies;
- availability of tools, plant and equipment needed to convert the materials, components and sub-assemblies at the workplace;

– availability of labour of the appropriate type, quality and quantity.

Chapter 7 discusses in detail how these objectives may be met. The purpose of labour at the preparation stage is to ensure that the flow of materials, components and sub-assemblies across the site to the building is maintained and it is usually necessary on a large job to dedicate part of the labour force to this end. The key links and roles may be illustrated thus:

delivery → storage → handling → assembly
(checker)→ (storekeeper) → (plant operator)

Since management's role is to ensure that these links are maintained unbroken, it must decide correctly whether the tasks should be specialised, or whether what are essentially non-productive roles can be combined with productive ones, if not throughout the job, then at particular stages. For example, the roles of checker and storekeeper may be combined, or the plant operator may spend part of his time contributing to the actual assembly process, as when driving the crane or the dumper.

**(b)  Tools and plant**   To maintain the flow of materials, components and sub-assemblies into the growing building, tools and plant are required. The first essential is that these should be of the correct type and specification for the job, the second that there should be a sufficient number of them and the third that they should be versatile. If these criteria are not observed, there is a risk that components and sub-assemblies will be damaged, with resulting cost and delay. For example, it is common practice, especially with smaller contractors, to use the dumper as a maid-of-all-work, for carrying concrete at one moment and roof trusses the next. This is understandable, since one or two versatile items of plant are both more useful and more affordable then several specialised ones, but, in the case of the roof trusses, ill-advised, since plates may be sprung or strained. It is necessary, also, to ensure that tools and plant can be operated in their appropriate environments, for example by providing level surfaces for road vehicles, proper manouvering spaces between buildings and storage areas and sawdust extraction plant in sawmills and joiners' shops. The equipment must be placed in the hands of trained operators and to this end management should ensure that plant is selected which can be used by the skills available, or failing this, that operatives can be trained in its use or obtained from elsewhere. More positively, management should be fully aware of the potential of modern plant in assisting materials' flow. For example, crane selection can greatly affect both speed and versatility of handling, in such matters as degree of mobility across the site, reach and luffing ability. Similarly, skid-steer loaders and forward-reach fork lifts make rapid handling within limited spaces and direct handling onto scaffolds possible, whilst the combination of ready-mixed concrete and rapid handling of the concrete to the workplace by means of pump or crane dramatically reduces the time between delivery and placing. Unfortunately, it is not always possible to make the ideal tools and items of plant available. The required item may be in use already on another site (this is where versatility becomes important), or sub-contractors may demand that certain items are made available to them as a condition of contract, which can interfere with the overall plant management strategy. Furthermore, the building itself may inhibit efficient plant use. For instance, there is often difficulty in transferring components horizontally into and within a multi-storey building once the frame has been enclosed. The rapid vertical movement by crane, which enables efficient placement whilst the frame is open, is no longer possible and expedients such as hoists and scaffolding towers must be resorted to.

Many items must be transferred into the building and stored near the workplace ready for assembly, for example plasterboards, partitioning components and heating and ventilation equipment. The choice lies between fixed or mobile cranes and hoists, the former able to work directly between delivery vehicles or storage areas and the building, the latter requiring intermediate handling with plant such as the fork lift. Cranes require off-loading points such as scaffold towers and the hoist has limited working capacity, but both may be required in the same building, especially when overloads are likely to occur. A further problem is the limited headroom and cluttered floor space likely to occur during assembly, making the horizontal movement of bulky items difficult.

# 7 Assembly

So far, 'assembly' has been defined as that activity which results in the completion of the next stage in the conversion process: materials are converted into components by assembling the range of constituent materials needed to form the component, components into sub-assemblies similarly. The final stage is reached when the sub-assemblies are brought together at the workplace and assembled into the growing building and it is this stage which is discussed in this chapter.

Preparation, if it is to be successful, must ensure that the materials, components and sub-assemblies can be assembled into the building in the most efficient and economic way. In other words:
- the necessary materials, components and sub-assemblies must be available at the workplace;
- the necessary conversions must have been completed;
- appropriate labour must be available;
- appropriate tools, plant and equipment must be available;
- there must be sufficient time allowed to carry out the work.

But although buildability at the assembly stage is dependent upon sound preparation, equally important is the fact that, unlike previous stages in the conversion process, this final stage usually takes place where the building is actually sited: except for portable or mobile buildings, everything necessary for assembly must be brought to the building, whereas at a number of previous stages the component or sub-assembly could be moved to where further materials or components could be added to it, as in a production line. From this, certain consequences follow:
- (a) a simple design will be easier to assemble than a complex one;
- (b) as much assembly as possible should be carried out under controlled conditions, for example in the least hostile physical environment;
- (c) the preparation for assembly, whilst thorough, should be minimised, for example by simplifying scaffolding and formwork and by avoiding excessive labour or tools, plant and equipment (chapter 6);
- (d) a continuous flow of materials, components and sub-assemblies into the building should be maintained;
- (e) the works should be accurately set out.

Considering these points in detail:

## (a) Simplicity in design

It has already been demonstrated (chapter 1) that uniqueness can be achieved by assembling similar components in a variety of ways: the 'Rubik-cube' concept. This makes uniqueness relatively cheap, since repetition can be practised in the design and assembly of the individual's components. Once the final assembly stage is reached, however, a problem arises: usually it is impossible to carry out the assembly even of highly repetitive components in situ with the same degree of accuracy as would be possible within the controlled environment of the factory or workshop: there may be too little working room, handling of many small components across site can lead to loss or damage, and so on. Furthermore, the specialised labour and tools needed to carry out complex conversions in the most efficient manner possible may not be available or practicable at the workplace, requiring their own specialised environments: robotised assembly, CAD/CAM processes, vacuum forming, pressing and casting are examples of this. A principle of buildability at the assembly stage, therefore, is to ensure that as much complex conversion as possible takes place prior to final assembly in the building and that this work is carried out in its most appropriate environment. The only constraint upon this principle is that imposed by delivery and handling: if sub-assemblies become too bulky, or are too fragile, they must be 'knocked down' or delivered in such a form that they can be reassembled or converted to fit as near to their final point of assembly as possible. Furthermore, specialised delivery and handling equipment may be necessary, such as low-loaders and heavy cranes, the use of which may negate some of the advantages of pre-assembly. Other factors to be considered include the achievement of maximum value per vehicle load and, a frequent corollary of this, the largest number of components which can be carried by any one vehicle. The following are the main factors which must be considered when evaluating the necessary degree of pre-assembly:

– number of components in the sub-assembly;
– interchangeability of components;
– size and handleability of components;
– simplicity and universality of interfacing and fixing components;
– amount of labour required to assemble;
– skills of labour required;
– tools and equipment required to assemble;
– time required to assemble;
– effects on adjacent components and sub-assemblies.

Interfacing and fixing components should obey the same buildability laws as primary and secondary components. In their cases also, simplicity in design enables maximal versatility and minimal variety and number of different components to be achieved. Jointing parallel timber boards illustrates the need for careful evaluation of assembly method, in relation both to this point and to the 'trade-off' between on- and off-site conversion:

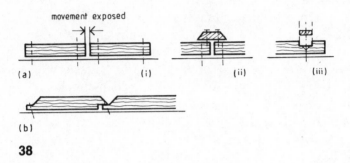

**38**

In diagram 38(a), two boards (primary components) can be butt jointed (i), but at the expense of movement in the joint. A better solution is shown in (ii), where a cover strip masks the joint, but this may not solve the problem of fixings, to which the solution may be either deliberately expressed fixings, such as cups and screws, or recessed and pelleted screws (iii). Although the primary components are simple in section, the complete sub-assembly, which may have to be carried out on the building, is relatively complex, requiring additional interfacing components and assembly activities. By comparison, the standard tongued and grooved board, self aligning and with concealed fixing components, is simple to assemble in situ, the complex profile having been formed in the factory (diagram 38(b)).

During design, it is essential to consider which assembly processes take place at which stage in the conversion sequence (diagram 31), with a view to simplifying final assembly, and to modify designs where assembly will be complex and expensive. For example, services' pipework and trunking are likely to relate closely to partitioning systems and all can be complicated by badly located structural members. If the structure can not be altered, then conversion of the three components and sub-assemblies will probably have to take place either in the site workshop or at the workplace itself. In these circumstances, it would be wrong to specify preformed manufactured units, such as proprietary partitioning systems, which are difficult to alter, and right to specify relatively small, modular units, easily adaptable to a variety of different circumstances. Better still, would be to design structure, services and partitioning systems as an integrated whole, thereby ensuring that, provided tolerances have been observed, fit will be achieved without alteration being necessary.

## (b) **Assembly under controlled conditions**

Assembly often has to take place under difficult conditions, for example because working space is cramped or because of exposure to weather. There are three assembly environments where especially hostile conditions may be found: below ground, in the exterior fabric of the building and internally, where atmospheres may become dusty, dirty and contaminated.

**Below ground level**, problems occur where excavation and assembly activities have to be performed in confined, dirty and wet spaces. For example, excavation should be minimised, since it takes time, involves the removal and storage of spoil and often necessitates working in poor conditions, resulting in inaccuracy and, sometimes, in danger. Fortunately, many methods now exist for mitigating the effects of below-ground working, including alternative foundation systems such as rafts or piles, the rapid excavation of narrow trenches and their immediate backfilling with concrete, remote controlled pipelaying and the safe retention of trench sides where entry by operatives is unavoidable. As elsewhere, buildability is served if the variety of activities is reduced and repetition is practised. For example, excavators work best in straight lines, with sufficient space allowed on either side of trenches for tracks and wheels to run without risking the collapse of adjacent trenches: frequent changes of direction or of bucket width cause delay and large areas may have to be excavated where the safe excavation of individual trenches is impossible. Similarly, piling is a systematic process, using relatively unwieldy and expensive plant, and pile layouts should reflect the likely order of work. Again, since it is simpler for plant to excavate trenches than holes, pad foundations are best formed by casting into formwork erected on trench bottoms, the spaces between pads probably being necessary anyway for tie beams. Equally, where excavation can not be avoided by piling or rafting, as in basement construction, it is often better to sheet pile before clearing and draining the whole area, leaving plenty of room for retaining walls, foundations, slabs and services without risking collapse or flooding.

**Above ground level**, assembly problems are created by weather and access, but the effects of these factors upon different forms of construction vary markedly. For instance, monolithic systems such as masonry, because progress is relatively slow and the materials and components are affected by weather until assembled, suffer maximal exposure and therefore the greatest risk of losing quality. From the buildability point of view, such systems should be avoided or minimised, or at least taken off the critical path, as in timber frame assembly. If they must be used, however, a number of methods exist for protecting both work and operatives. For example, the assembly area or workplace can be enclosed within a temporary building, this being enlarged or moved as the permanent building within it grows. Although this technique is relatively expensive, the cost will be offset in part by improved productivity resulting from the better working environment. A simpler, less effective but more affordable alternative is to fix protective sheeting to the scaffolding, this keeping off the worst of the wind and rain. A third alternative is to increase the rate of assembly, thereby getting the job done quicker. Unless prefabricated masonry sections are used, however, this involves either employing more labour or simplifying the work so as to make assembly easier; the possibility of designing the masonry to be non-structural, thereby taking it off the critical path, has already been mentioned.

Frames can be assembled quickly, but during the assembly sequences there is a necessarily high exposure to weather and to the risk of injury. Nevertheless, a number of measures can be taken to minimise these risks and to improve buildability at the same time. For example, the number of separate components in the frame sub-assembly can be reduced, by using vertical members extending through several floors and by attaching as many interfacing and fixing components as possible to the primary ones, either at ground level or off-site before delivery. 'Platform' assembly, as used in timber and in situ reinforced concrete frames, enables assembly to proceed safely floor by floor, and it is technically possible to assemble large elements of structure at ground level before pitching or jacking them into position. Furthermore, it is becoming economic to assemble primary frame components to each other in semi-automated ways, for example by using beam manipulators to lift and place beams accurately adjacent to columns, leaving the operatives the relatively simple task of inserting and tightening bolts and nuts. Operative safety is also being improved by the greatly extended reach and versatility of 'cherry picker' mobile cranes, by the use of composite floor decks in steel frame construction and by the provision and enforcement of the use of safety equipment. Rate of assembly of steel frames is increased by specifying modular, dry casings rather than in situ concrete ones, by casting on casings off-site or by using spray-on coatings, application of which can now also be automated where frame layouts are simple.

Cladding is a vital element in the building as far as expense is concerned, since it forms the boundary between the external and internal environments: its assembly may be difficult, but once it is in place and the building has been made watertight, work inside can proceed within a predictable environment. Systems should, therefore, be modular and quick to assemble, criteria not met ideally by masonry components: when these are used to clad multi-storey frames, the commencement of services, partitioning and finishes depends upon the completion floor by floor of, usually, brick and block spandrels and glazing units. Since these are on the critical paths for the sub-assemblies mentioned and since the assembly sequence of masonry is necessarily relatively slow, poor buildability here can seriously delay progress. It is preferable, therefore, to consider large panel methods, such as precast concrete units or pre-assembled, glazed wall systems, although these, too, have their disadvantages: the former are heavy and require skilled handling into the building (chapter 6), the latter, consisting of many small components which must be assembled accurately to each other, are better fitted together at ground level and lifted into place as major sub-assemblies. Precast panels should be tolerance compatible with the frame and fixable from inside the building to minimise operative risk and the need for scaffolding. The same is true of glazed wall sub-assemblies, bearing in mind that the handling of these may be especially difficult, both because of their inherent fragility and because they are easily stressed and distorted during lifting and placing. It is common practice, in fact, to fit glazing separately from its surrounding panel or frame to minimise risk of damage. Where this is done, the units must be handled into position near the point of assembly, more easily done inside the building than onto scaffolding. This implies internal fixing, desirable anyway for ease of replacement, and the completion of at least the sub-floor, to provide a level surface for handling and storage. On balance, it is probably better to pre-fix glazing at ground level, when panel distortion during lifting can be controlled, and to protect adequately against accidental breakage. In this way, the building is enclosed in one operation and the problems of storing and fixing sometimes heavy glazing units from spaces where there may be limited working room are avoided.

The assembly of roof structures and finishes presents some of the most exposed and hazardous working conditions in the building. Structures, for example in pitched and hipped roofs, can be complex, involving the assembly of many relatively small components such as trusses, purlins, rafters and edge members. Again, the principle of ground level or off-site sub-assembly should be observed, complete sections of roof being lifted into place in many fewer operations. In this way, tolerances can be better controlled and the number of interfacing and fixing components at the point of final assembly greatly reduced. The early completion of roof finishes is vital: only once these are in place can the building be dried out and internal finishing begin. Traditional components such as tiles and slates are not well suited to rapid assembly and are not ideal, therefore, from the buildability viewpoint. Although adaptable and able to be fitted to relatively complex roof forms, they consist of many small parts, which must be stored and handled with varying degrees of care and difficulty. Furthermore, their final assembly into the building takes place in conditions of maximal exposure to the weather and often at high risk to the operatives. For this reason, ways should be sought of improving their buildability, for example by using temporary enclosures, by specifying fewer, larger components, by designing simpler roof forms or by using pre-formed interfacing and fixed components, such as 'dry' ridges and verges.

Sheet roofing systems, on the other hand, enable large areas to be rendered weathertight speedily and are, therefore, especially well suited to big roofs of simple form. Since they are light, they require lighter supporting structures, depending upon span and wind loading, but they can be difficult to assemble: large sheets are easily caught by the wind and access for operatives can be tricky, since supporting structures are slender and spaced some distance apart. Complex profiles require matching and cutting and both these activities and the fixing of sheets using screws and bolts means manipulating power tools in sometimes difficult conditions.

Flat roofing systems, whether felts or asphalts, suffer from the same buildability problems as tiles and slates: many separate components and sub-assemblies, which must be handled into position at the top of the building and applied under sometimes difficult working conditions. From the buildability viewpoint, therefore, such systems should be avoided, or at least designed so as to minimise complexity, for example by simplifying the design of cross-falls or reducing the number of layers in multi-layer decks.

The final stage in building assembly is the application of finishes, including pointing, sealing, painting and staining. All these activities may have to take place when operatives are exposed to the weather and when the achievement of controlled working conditions is difficult. Problems can be avoided or simplified in a number of ways, however: the pointing of facing brickwork can take place as work proceeds, sealing is now a rapid operation with modern equipment, but can often be 'designed out' anyway by specifying 'zip-in' gaskets, painting can be replaced by stains or self-finishing with anodised or plastic coatings, or components can simply be left self-finished, where surface treatment has taken weathering properly into account.

**Dusty, dirty and contaminated atmospheres** make assembly difficult and provide sometimes serious safety hazards. The main problems arise from cutting, drilling and chasing and from the use of toxic materials,[1] the result in turn of having to convert materials, components and sub-assemblies at the workplace to ensure fit. Much can be done, therefore, to reduce hazard by designing and preparing carefully and assembling accurately, for example by applying foresight to the distribution of electrical services within the wall thickness or by respecting tolerances and traditional working practices. Not all conversion at the workplace is objectionable,

[1] Curwell and March: *Hazardous building materials: a guide to the selection of alternatives* Spon; London, 1986.

indeed much is unavoidable, for example when cutting and jointing screwed steel pipework, and the enclosed building environment may be entirely suitable for this activity. Both components and tools have been developed which have compatible relationships, making cutting and fitting straightforward, and some components require very little further conversion before being finally assembled, for example when pipework is supplied in standard modular lengths or can be jointed on the 'push-fit' principle. Good preparation, however, can obviate much workplace adaptation, conversion taking place in the environment best suited to it in the factory or workshop and if this is followed by accurate assembly, with tolerances closely observed, the chances of having to make major alterations to ensure fit are substantially reduced.

The cutting of materials and components can be defined under three headings: drilling, shaping and shortening. Some of these adaptations can take place prior to handling to the workplace, for example the drilling of bolt holes in steel plates and the shaping of timber into window frame sections, but others can only be carried out at the workplace. The work involved generates waste, noise and dust and can cause injury from failure or mishandling of tools and from flying particles. It is essential therefore that, where such work in unavoidable, the correct tools, correctly prepared, sharpened and guarded are used, that operatives are trained in their use and that protective clothing is worn.

One of the least desirable forms of adaptation is chasing. When cutting relatively large amounts of waste from dry materials, large quantities of dust and particles are produced, resulting in major local pollution. Yet this is one of the operations most easily avoided by careful design and preparation, for example by providing ducts and conduits, routing pipes and wires through voids rather than wall thicknesses or by locating finishes proud of wall surfaces to enable wires to be surface fixed. Where chasing is unavoidable, protective clothing, ventilation and even the forced extraction of dust and particles are essential.

Finally, toxic materials present a major hazard, since they can be ingested, inhaled or absorbed through the skin.[1] Materials most likely to cause problems include plastics such as pvc, polystyrene, polyurethane and urea-formaldehyde, composites of plastics and other materials, wood preservatives, insecticides, fungicides and adhesives. Assembly must take place in a properly ventilated atmosphere and operatives should wear protective clothing, including over-garments, gloves and face-masks. Again, good preparation can prevent much difficulty, for example by pre-assembling laminated panels and pre-treating timber.

[1] Curwell and March: *Hazardous building materials: a guide to the selection of alternatives* Spon; London, 1986.

## (c) Minimising preparation for assembly

Although proper preparation is vital in ensuring that final assembly can proceed smoothly and without incurring the risks referred to earlier, it is important not to complicate procedures and equipment unduly and to maintain adequate but not excessive resources of management, labour, and plant. Furthermore, in accordance with the principles of buildability, the number of new assembly methods adopted on any one job should be limited. Where new methods are unavoidable, adequate training should be provided, followed by the maximum of replication to ensure the greatest possible capitalisation on new knowledge.

With regard to temporary works and equipment, a balance has to be struck between the need to assist and protect labour whilst it is carrying out assembly activities and the costs of maintaining such works in position. This issue was discussed in the previous chapter, where, for example, the diseconomies of complex scaffolding and formwork, of scaffolding having to be retained in position owing to out of sequence assembly and of temporary accesses were pointed out (diagrams 36 and 37).

Management is deeply involved with all aspects of the job and crucially with the assembly stage. Managers are dedicated to efficient, cost-effective operation and to minimising inputs to achieve particular ends. This applies as much to the preparation for assembly as to the assembly activity itself. For example, where assembly is likely to be complex, preparation will have to be carried out with care to ensure efficient resourcing. This may involve setting up training programmes or special stock control procedures, where the amount and repetitive nature of the new work justifies it, or alternatively buying-in the requisite skills and equipment when an activity is more 'one-off'. Versatility is a key factor here: not only plant and equipment but labour also may be adaptable to new roles with relatively modest amounts of input. Ways of controlling complexity at the preparation stage include:
– breaking activities down into manageable elements;
– identifying and sharing common features between elements, thereby enabling better resource utilisation to be achieved;
– buying-in labour and equipment where assembly will be 'one-off', as, for example, with lift installation;
– setting up procedures for controlling special sub-contractors and suppliers;
– regarding re-design at a late stage in the job as very much a last resort (the latest time for this is at tender and contract stages).

When labour has to be trained or retrained specially to enable assembly to be carried out, time will be lost and extra costs will accrue to the job. Preparation therefore requires job analysis to establish whether or not such extra expense is justified. It may not be if assembly methods using standard procedures can be devised, requiring minimal retraining of staff or the buying-in of extra skills. For example, a timber stair becomes a relatively complex item if winders have to be cut and fitted on site: instead of a simple, bought-in sub-assembly, which can be installed by a woodworker of modest skill levels, separate components have to be provided and fitted by a more highly qualified woodworker, thereby incurring the extra costs of storage, handling and special labour. The problem could be avoided by redesigning the building to accommodate a simple stair. Once tasks have been broken down into manageable elements, it is sensible to ensure that the work is repeated as often as possible to make maximal effective use of new knowledge gained. Care should be taken to avoid excessive repetition, however, since boredom can set in causing quality to suffer.

Similar arguments apply to the specification and use of tools and plant. Special tools and plant are usually only justified if they meet the following criteria:
– speed preparation and assembly significantly beyond the rate which would be achieved using standard items;
– reduce the number of stages in the preparation process;
– substitute effectively for special or expensive labour;
– represent gains to the tool and plant inventory as a whole;
– improve operative safety levels.

Examples of the appropriate use of special equipment include concrete pumps in locations where cranes can not be used and the volume to be placed is large, the automated assembly of complex components and work which has to be carried out in hazardous environments.

Finally, preparation for assembly can be minimised if the temptation to introduce new assembly methods is resisted. Such methods can usually only be justified if new problems must be solved in new ways, if real savings in time and cost can be achieved or if the techniques and skills acquired can be replicated, either by personnel themselves or by knowlege transfer to other members of the building team. In this last respect, it may not be necessary to capitalise on the particular job in hand: knowledge transferred into the company's 'knowledge bank' can be extremely useful in increasing versatility, provided it can be accessed easily.

### (d) Maintaining the flow of materials, components and sub-assemblies into the growing building
For assembly to proceed smoothly and without interruption, the flow of materials, components and sub-assemblies to the workplace must be maintained. This can only happen if the following criteria are satisfied:
– the assembly sequence has been accurately planned and programmed;

- the appropriate type, quality and quantity of labour have been made available;
- the appropriate type, quality and quantity of tools, plant and equipment have been provided;
- management input has been sufficient;
- the appropriate working environment has been provided.

**Accurately planning and programming the assembly sequence**   These are critical activities, since failure will have repercussions on other parts of the job, will result in delay and can affect morale. Incorrect assembly, which can take place either because of ignorance or of lack of care, will mean that:
- fitting components together is either impossible or poorly done;
- time is wasted adapting components so that they can be fitted;
- materials, components and sub-assemblies may not perform in the manner intended;
- the work sequence is interrupted, with some activities being repeated unnecessarily;
- the wrong components may be provided for the revised work sequence, resulting in the need to order new components and return the original ones to store;
- labour, tools, plant and equipment may not be capable of assembling the components in the new ways.

In tackling these problems, it is essential first to adopt a broad strategy, a method of approach to assembly problems. At this strategic level, decisions will have to be taken about, for example, the phasing of assembly of major sub-assemblies, such as the separate buildings within a complex, about the divisions between horizontal and vertical assembly sequences and about sequences of completing structure, cladding, services and finishes. The implications of these stategic decisions for the tactics of detailed assembly will also have to be considered. Various decision and planning aids may be available to assist. For example, the building owner may have requirements affecting order of handover and this can be reflected in the design, which would enable certain parts to be completed in their entirety whilst work was continuing elsewhere. The design itself may enforce certain assembly strategies, depending upon the structural or cladding systems or the materials and components chosen. The contractor may prefer certain assembly methods, suited to his organisation, which will guide decision-taking, especially when related to the possibly conflicting demands of sub-contractors.

Once the main strategic decisions have been taken, planning can move to the tactical level. For example, a decision to phase will have repercussions for the preparation stages and for the provision of temporary works, plant and equipment. Thus, although it may be necessary to retain expensive equipment on site for a longer period, it may be possible to use less of it by moving it from phase to phase serially as work is completed. Alternatively, where the use of expensive plant can not be avoided, it may be better to use it to assemble those parts for which it is intended in all phases, rather to remove it from the site and bring it back again. This might apply to the erection of steel, multi-storey frames or the installation of special items of air handling equipment, for example. Another tactical decision will be concerned with protection of the works during assembly. Often, the building itself can be used to offer protection, as when the early roofing of an industrial shed enables the ground floor slab to be cast protected from the elements, or when partition units can be stored and assembled in the dry floorspaces afforded by early completion of the cladding. Again, temporary works can affect assembly procedures and sequences, as when the location and erection of scaffolding interferes with the handling and fixing of cladding (diagram 36) or when temporary accesses must be provided for items of plant such as compressors and pumps (diagram 35). Sub-contractors' working methods may differ from those of the main contractor, requiring special attendance or agreement on both sides to modify practices and firm management is essential here if programmes are not to fall behind. Finally, the feasibility of assembly procedures may have to be tested, for example by work study analysis or the construction of mock-ups, prior to actual assembly in the building. The essential need is to ensure that time and cost are properly controlled, whether by using conventional planning aids such as bar charts and networks, or by the more sophisticated methods just referred to.

**Making the appropriate type, quality and quantity of labour available** It was pointed out in chapter 6 that sufficient labour must be available at all stages of preparation, from delivery to assembly, and that this labour should be of the appropriate type and quality. Only when this had been done could the flow of materials and components be maintained. For the same reason, the personnel used at the assembly stage must be sufficient for the work in hand, should have access to and be capable of using the right tools and equipment and should be so organised that they are neither overworked nor standing around idle. This is an ideal almost impossible to achieved, but some of the reasons why things go wrong can be identified:
– *job behind programme*: this often results in the job being flooded with labour, it having been calculated that it is cheaper to do this than to incur damages for late completion. Unfortunaely, the tactic may be self defeating, since tasks can absorb only so much extra input and quality

may suffer if untried labour is introduced. Good buildability can assist here by ensuring that tasks are manageable within labour constraints and that, once learnt, are repeated;

- *plant management defective*: if plant is overloaded, alternative handling methods may have to be introduced, some of which may be labour intensive. This infringes the principle of tool substitution, resulting in inefficiency;

- *assembly more difficult than anticipated*: one result of poor buildability may be that more operatives are needed to complete an assembly activity than were envisaged during preparation. This can have repercussions elsewhere in the job, for example if operatives have to be taken off other work or if such work has to be delayed or altered;

- *labour incompetent*: until experience has been gained of an operative's ability, or lack of it, it is difficult to judge his performance accurately. If his ability is below standard, it may incur a financial penalty to replace him, both in terms of delay and sometimes of making good shoddy work. Furthermore, low performance by operatives may result in employing more of them than the task warrants;

- *preparation inadequate*: if the chain of support extending from the factory to the workplace is weak or breaks, operatives dedicated to assembly may have to perform some of the tasks which should be carried out by the 'preparation force'. For example, craftsmen may have to carry brick from the packs as well as lay them, or drive fork-life trucks on site transit handling duties. This is inefficient on two counts: it breaks the work sequence and uses high grade staff for low grade tasks;

- *tools inefficient or of the wrong type:* apart from slowing down the work-rate, resulting in more labour being employed than would otherwise be necessary, the wrong tools can cause frustration, thereby lowering morale and reducing the quality of work;

- *poor relationships between general and sub-contractors' labour*: sub-contractors are responsible to their own organisations and work according to the constraints of those organisations. Apart from problems of dual management which can arise from this, working practices may differ, affecting standards, assembly methods and timing.

**Ensuring that the appropriate type, quality and quantity of tools, plant and equipment are made available**   The discussion about tool substitution has been presented in an earlier chapter, the principle being that tools can take the place of labour and that the balance between the two will reflect the relative costs of each in differing circumstances. During assembly, therefore:

- sufficient tools should be available for the job in hand;
- an accurate relationship between tools and labour must be established,

in terms of working rate and the ability of labour to use tools to their optimal capacity; in other words, tools should be neither more nor less sophisticated than necessary and they should not stand idle or be misused;

— tools should be of sufficient quality for the task in hand and capable of assisting in the assembly of components at the agreed quality levels;
— tools should be versatile, enabling a wide range of assembly operations to be carried out using a limited range of tools;
— tool maintenance should be straightforward, with wearing parts either 'universalised' (easily replaceable from a wide range of sources) or capable of being maintained on or near to the job.

The reasons why performance can suffer correspond to those listed earlier for labour. For example, extra labour required to complete a job or programme will require extra tools, plant and equipment. When tools are personal, this may not matter, but fixed plant such as cranes and hoists can become overworked, causing delay. This is a function of effective plant management, which is concerned with resource smoothing to eliminate peaks and troughs and which should be able to foresee when overloading is likely. Another cause of difficulty is those assembly operations which are hard to perform, requiring extra or special tools to complete them. Such tools may not be readily available, or may require special training in their use, all adding to cost. In fact, the matching of operative skill to tool capability is important, as has already been mentioned, and this is as much a function of component design as of poor buildability during the assembly process itself. For example, where vertical pipe runs have not been located exactly on the drawing, special holes may have to be drilled through sub-assemblies such as floors using expensive hole-cutters; these may demand not only a remote power supply but also careful handling. Other reasons for poor performance from tools, plant and equipment include inadequate preparation, requiring perhaps extra tools to complete that assembly stage and demands made by sub-contractors for more or different tools from those which had been envisaged during planning. Finally, good build-ability at the assembly stage recognises that tools, plant and equipment are a valuable resource, the misuse of which will result in premature failure and high maintenance costs. It recognises that ease of assembly is reflected in minimal labour and tool input for a given result and that creative management, which sees for example that extensive workplaces can make the use of larger or more sophisticated machines possible, is a valuable investment.

**Providing sufficient management input** Assuming that the preparation stage has been completed efficiently, a smooth flow of materials, components and sub-assemblies will be directed towards the growing build-ing. It is management's job to ensure that assembly into the building is carried out as expeditiously as possible. The reasons why this may not happen have already been described. In summary, these include the type, quantity and quality of labour, tools, plant and equipment, the quality of preparation and the suitability of the workplace for the conversion and assembly activities which will take place there. Much the most important of these factors, however, is the nature, ability and motivation of the operative actually performing the assembly task. Usually, work will be supervised by a foreman or chargehand, the site manager or his deputy or by the operative himself. It is desirable in management terms that, as far as possible, the operative manages his own work, since he then controls the work and sets his own standards. Craftsmen traditionally work in this way, often setting themselves up in business in order to ensure independence and freedom from centalised control. Unfortunately, work can not always proceed with so few constraints: tasks may be exceptionally complex or extensive, requiring a team of people, some with special skills; operatives may be poor self-managers, only able to work comfortably when relieved of administrative or decision-making roles; central management may itself be poor at recognising an operative's need for independence; morale on site may be poor, resulting in suspicion and mistrust and poor quality work. It is management's job to identify such potential difficulties early and to find solutions. For example, complex work can be broken down into simpler 'packages', bringing it within the ability range of the operative, or, when particularly high quality work is demanded, substi-tuting personnel with the appropriate skills. It may even be possible to redesign or respecify work to a lower level of constructional difficulty: when it is remembered that difficult-to-assemble components slow the rate of build and increase costs, this may be an attractive alternative. The operative who is a poor self manager must be dealt with tactfully, either by moving him to other work, or by relieving him with his agreement, usually gladly given, of the parts of the job which he finds tedious or incompre-hensible. Weak central management can badly affect morale. If this syndrome affects only one site, then corrective action may be possible without threatening overall viability; if it is general, the existence of the firm itself may be threatened. There are many reasons for poor morale on site: late changes in design, requiring work to be dismantled and rebuilt, poor management, poor buildability. During assembly, the effects of poor management will become apparent and it is essential for this reason to ensure that the correct management input is made at this stage.

**Providing the appropriate environment for assembly to take place**   Assembly can be carried out in one of three ways: linear, selective or batch. In the first of these, components are picked and fitted together from lines of similar components without regard to fit, the next component in the line always being taken; the second method requires the assembler to pick and choose between sets of similar components to ensure that the best possible fit is achieved; the third method again selects components at random, without regard to fit, but this time from batches of similar components rather than from lines. Examples of the first method would be picking a brick from a stack, of the second, fitting a piston in a cylinder and of the third, using bolts, nuts and washers to make fixings. Each method is appropriate for a particular type of assembly operation, but each may require a different working environment.

Labour, tools, plant and equipment are most efficiently employed when they are working continuously on the tasks to which they are best suited. The working environment during assembly is important, therefore. For instance, in a limited working environment, in which only one task at a time may be completed, or in which one work section must be completed before another can be started, labour may either have to perform tasks to which it is unsuited, or there may be delays whilst operatives wait for other interdependent tasks to be completed. In an extensive working environment, on the other hand, in which tasks are available at all levels, personnel can move around and can afford to specialise. The limited environment encourages, indeed demands, versatility and tolerance of a degree of inefficiency, the extensive environment specialism and well organised working sequences. It is management's job to create the appropriate working environment for the assembly operations to be carried out, taking into account the assembly method necessary, whether linear, selective or batch, the personnel to be employed and the tools, plant and equipment which they will use. To demonstrate these principles, one could instance the building of facing brickwork walls. The walls may be assembled from ground to eaves by one gang of craftsmen and labourers. Components must be picked in order from a pile of identical components and assembled repetitively until the wall is complete. Since other trades are dependent on the bricklayers, the latter must work in the same limited environment, doing work that is both difficult and easy, until the work section is finished. Any shortage of bricks or other components will delay assembly. An alternative way of working, however, is to allow the bricklayers to move round the building, or indeed round a series of buildings, dividing the work between them in such a way that the most skilled men do the difficult parts, the apprentices the easy ones, each able to select the components from larger or more varied piles. In this way, the work becomes more specialised, better matched to the skills available, and proceeds continuously, since baulking at one location simply means that the workplace moves elsewhere.

## (e) Setting out the building accurately

Proper assembly depends upon accurate setting out, not only of the site and of the buildings on it, but also of the physical environment within which the buildings are to be built. Without proper setting out, buildability is compromised, since components and sub-assemblies will not fit and this is as true of the relationships between adjacent buildings, or between offices, compounds, fixed plant and accesses, as it is between, say, structure and cladding panels.

**Setting out the site**   Many of the issues affecting site buildability were discussed in chapter 2. When it comes to setting out the site and to locating the buildings accurately upon it, a number of problems emerge. For example, the building may have a hard-to-measure relationship to the National Grid, making its initial location difficult; roads may be designed with compound curves, making the establishing of centres and the measuring of radii a complex business; the form of the building itself may be hard to describe at ground level, especially when the site slopes; cumulative errors may build up across the site, or, with buildings set at different angles to each other, their exact relationship may become a question of trial and error; finally, design changes may throw out all previous calculations and make certain 'fixes' impossible.

Solutions must be sought mainly in common sense and simplicity. For example, personnel carrying out the work should be properly trained and should use the correct instruments for the work in hand; site layout drawings should show National Grid References umabiguously, together with dimensional offsets and angular displacements; curves should be single-radius ones wherever possible, measurable from an accessible point; level changes should be few in number and connected by simple gradients, not only to ease setting out, but also to improve buildability; once fixed, survey points should be recorded and clearly marked and not easily disturbed by personnel or passing site traffic; late changes in design, if inevitable, should be agreed between designer and contractor so that the full implications can be considered.

Buildability at this stage is affected as much by conditions below ground as by those above. A building may be set out with subtlety and accuracy at ground level, but have to be moved once excavation reveals unforeseen problems, such as the existence of old basements, mine shafts or polluted ground. Accurate sub-ground investigation is essential, therefore, before final decisions are made about building location. Similarly, cognisance should be taken of overhead obstructions, such as wires, posts and trees and of structures adjacent to the site, especially other buildings and where the working room required by plant such as tower cranes will be affected.

Another factor is deciding appropriate degrees of accuracy. For example, whereas on open, rural sites a tolerance in setting out of ± 250 mm may be acceptable, on city centre sites, surrounded by buildings and streets, the tolerance may be as little as ± 10 mm. It follows that both personnel and equipment must be capable of working at the required level of accuracy, failure here resulting possibly in redesign, the readjustment of planned tolerances or even the remanufacture of components and sub-assemblies.

**Setting out the building** When setting out the building, accuracy assumes even greater importance, since tolerances will usually be much finer and the repercussions if inaccuracy occurs more severe. Initial setting out of foundations and substructures may vary however, since not all assemblies at this stage are equally critical. For example, wide strip footings allow some room for error, whilst trench fill and pad and pile foundations do not. In particular, where assemblies which have wide tolerances must lie adjacent to those which have fine ones, as when in situ work abuts precast or steel work, the finer tolerances must dictate the degree of care taken with the cruder construction. A further consideration here is that care taken with the principal sub-assemblies of the building will reflect in greater ease of assembly later on, and to ensure that the appropriate degrees of accuracy are being achieved, frequent checking is important: the task of the 'line and level' engineer is a vital one. Once the basic frame of the building has been plumbed and aligned accurately, to the requisite tolerance limits, it is used as the datum from which to establish the positions and alignments of all dependent components and sub-assemblies. Once again, since these will often require assembly to finer tolerances than the supporting structure, 'tolerance interfaces', or the ability to adjust between adjacent components so as to maintain tolerance compatibility, must be carefully designed and frequently checked.

**The physical environment of the site** Buildability is assisted if the physical environment of the site is conducive to ease of movement and to the maintaining of materials flow into the building. To this end, offices, compounds and fixed plant must be located conveniently and mobile plant must be able to move about the site economically and easily. Setting out therefore encompasses not only the location of the building and permanent roads and services within agreed degrees of accuracy, but also that of temporary roads, accesses offices, compounds, storage areas and plant. Various degrees of criticality apply here: storage areas may have flexible boundaries, reflecting their growth and contraction during the progress of the contract, whereas the exact location of site offices and tower cranes, dependent, for example, upon services connections and site coverage, may be important.

# 8 Buildability in use

During a building's life, it must be maintained to ensure optimal performance for its users and the maximum return when the time comes to sell it. Ease of maintenance and replacement are as much a function of performance and buildability as is initial assembly. To perform at the agreed quality level, a building must have durability, which is a measure therefore of a building's function and performance during its life. To be easy to maintain, that is to clean, repair and replace defective or worn out components, it must possess good 'buildability in use'.

Durability is assured by selecting the appropriate quality of materials, components and sub-assemblies during design and by replacing them with items of equal quality as the original ones break or wear out, subject to the estimated remaining life of the building: a building likely to be demolished within a short time does not need the best replacement parts. The word 'appropriate' signifies an accurate judgement about quality: too poor a component will fail prematurely, possibly damaging adjacent components when it does so; too good a component will be relatively expensive, may have too long a life and may even suffer damage from less good adjacent components. It is important, naturally, that interfacing and fixing components should have durabilities which are compatible with their adjacent primary components, especially where they are inaccessible: the 'nail sick' roofing slate may require the relaying of the entire roof. Furthermore, all materials, components and sub-assemblies should be required to perform only in the environments for which they were designed: the assumption that rain water is clean, for example, may be misplaced and if it contains salts or acids, breakdown of surface finishes will occur. Poor initial assembly can also seriously affect durability. For instance, wide tolerances may allow water to penetrate joints and creasing or scratching can allow rust to gain a hold. Although durability is mainly a performance related factor, therefore, design for good buildability in use can influence it significantly.

Where buildability in use is undoubtedly important is in the ease or otherwise of maintenance, both of the building as a whole and of its constituent parts. For maintenance to be effective, a number of criteria must be observed:

- there must be good access to those parts of the building requiring maintenance;
- such access must be safe;
- dismantling must be straightforward;
- it must be easy to fit the new parts;
- reassembly must be straightforward.

Where only *cleaning* is required, the need for this can usually be foreseen and allowed for in the original design, for example by providing gangways or cradles, but cleaning may sometimes extend beyond the routine when, say, water catching ledges have to be washed down to prevent acids attacking finishes. Buildability in use would obviate the need for this by ensuring that projections were properly weathered and therefore to some extent self-cleaning. *Repair* differs from cleaning, in that access for more sophisticated tools and equipment will be needed and that it must be physically possible to dismantle and replace components; this may require good lighting and protection from the weather whilst work is being carried out. *Replacement* is different again, in that new components or even sub-assemblies may have to be brought to the building and fitted. This may generate handling problems, where components are large, or even partial dismantling of the building itself in order to gain access (diagram 16(f)).

## Failure precedence

As a general principle, design should allow for 'failure precedence'. This ensures that parts which are cheap and easy to replace fail before those which are not. An example from a different technology is the automobile disc brake pad, which is designed to absorb the wear on the braking mechanism and to be easy to replace. Since replacement can take place almost indefinitely within the life of the vehicle without affecting other parts of the mechanism, those other parts can be relatively expensive and difficult to replace; the pads, in a sense, 'protect' the rest of the brake assembly. The principle can be extended further, however, for other parts of a component or sub-assembly will wear in due course and have to be replaced. In the disc brake example, the next component to wear after the pad will be the disc upon which the pad bears, followed perhaps by the hydraulic rubber seals, brake pipes and pistons. Ideally, as each component wears or fails, it should be possible to replace it without disturbing the other components, or at least only those components where periodic inspection or replacement are desirable anyway, but where this is not possible, the sequential dismantling required to gain access to the failed component should be straightforward. Diagram 39 illustrates the options:

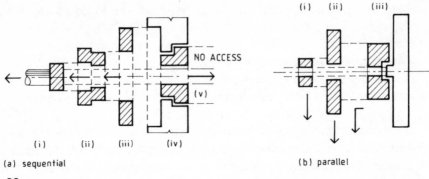

(a) sequential                                    (b) parallel

**39**

In (a), components can be dismantled sequentially from right to left, (i) being withdrawn from (ii), (ii) from (iii) and (iii) from (iv). Provided that this procedure is straightforward, it does not matter unduly in which of the components (i) to (iii) failure occurs, although it would be best if it occurred in (i) before (ii) and so on. The method breaks down only when one or more of the series of components cannot be dismantled easily: in this case, component (v) can only be dismantled from the reverse side of (iv), to which it is assumed no easy access is possible. An alternative approach is illustrated in (b), where sequential dismantling is not necessary: components (i), (ii) and (iii) can be withdrawn independently of each other, although where an interlock is required, as in (iii), the shaded secondary component would have to be moved backwards along the assembly's axis before it could be withdrawn – a matter of providing an appropriate tolerance. A practical example of the first of these principles in building would be where pipework ran behind dry-lining or in the thickness of a partition: whereas the components making up a surface-mounted fitting connected to the pipework could be unscrewed and removed sequentially, the pipe itself could be accessed only by removing a section of the dry lining; a leak there, apart from being hard to detect, would be difficult to repair.

**Maintenance; repair and replacement**

Buildability in use requires that, in addition to sensible design for failure precedence, maintenance should be possible using the labour, tools, plant and equipment likely to be available during the life of the building. The principle of 'universality' (chapter 1) is applicable here. For example, where dismantling and reassembly can be carried out at relatively low skill levels and using simple tools, the chances are that these resources will always be available. Conversely, complex, specialised maintenance is likely to be expensive and time consuming and in years to come may not be available at all. The principle of building up unique components and sub-assemblies from standardised parts, using relatively unskilled labour and simple tools, is therefore as applicable as it is to the original assembly. On the other hand, tools can be designed or adapted to enable obsolete components and their fixings to be maintained, albeit at a price. Where even this proves impossible, components and sub-assemblies may have to be discarded and rebuilt using up to date methods.

A similar argument applies to materials, components and sub-assemblies. Universal components, such as blocks, boards, plasters and screws, are always likely to be available. In any case, even if they are not, alternatives can be found which do not affect appearance or utility. Specialised components, on the other hand, may be impossible to replace or match in years to come. Into this category would fall facing bricks, roof tiles, stonework, radiators and the like. This may not matter if the life of the component is a long one, but when relatively frequent replacement is likely, or where the integrity of a primary component is likely to be threatened by failure of the secondary components from which it is assembled, resulting in the discarding of the primary component, buildability in use is important. For example, services are likely to be updated more than once in the life of a building, and window and doors almost as frequently. Modular replacement is desirable, therefore, enabling new secondary components to be fitted to old primary components or sub-assemblies without requiring the replacement of everything: new radiators or boilers should be matchable to existing pipework and new ironmongery to old doors and windows. To summarise, the principles of buildability in use, applied to materials, components and sub-assemblies, can be defined as follows:
- the use wherever possible of standard, 'universal' materials, components and sub-assemblies
- the containing of 'unique' components within 'standard' interfacing components (diagram 14(b)); the standardising of interfacing and fixing components especially so that, if 'specials' do have to be made, enough can be made to be economically sensible
- the avoidance of odd dimensions and modules
- the designing for 'failure precedence', as defined earlier.

Generally, those materials, components and sub-assemblies which are likely to fail or to require updating first, should be those to which access is easiest and the dismantling and reassembly of which, using the simplest of skills and labour, are the most straightforward. Designers can make a major contribution to buildability in use and, to exemplify the principles enumerated above, it is useful to examine the problems presented by *windows* during the life of a traditionally constructed building. Window maintenance can be defined under two headings, 'routine' and 'repair/replacement':

| Routine | Repair and replacement |
|---|---|
| Cleaning glass | Replacing glass |
| Cleaning frame | Repairing frame |
| Painting/staining frame | Replacing frame |
| Oiling hinges and catches | Replacing hinges and catches. |

These apparently straightforward activities present a number of problems, however. For example:

| | Problem |
|---|---|
| Cleaning glass | Gaining access to both sides |
| | Cleaning corners |
| Replacing glass | Gaining access to exterior if above ground level |
| | Removing glass safely |
| | Preparing rebate for new glass |
| Replacing frame | Separating frame from interfacing, fixing and adjacent primary components |
| | Obtaining suitable replacement frame |
| | Making good to damaged internal finishes. |

Applying the principles of buildability in use, solutions should be sought amongst the following possibilities:

| Activity | Possible solution |
|---|---|
| Cleaning glass | Provide safe access to exterior |
| | Ensure exterior reachable safely through opening light |
| | Specify reversible opening lights |
| Replacing glass | Provide safe access to exterior |
| | Ensure glazed areas within reach from the interior |
| | Glaze from inside building |
| | Specify reversible opening light |
| | Design glazing seals for easy removal and replacement using minimal labour and tools |
| | Ensure seals not 'over specialised', making replacement in later years difficult |

Replacing frame

Provide safe access to exterior
Ensure frames within reach from the interior
Design frames for easy removal from building
by:
– making internal removal and replacement
 possible
– designing for easy separation from wall or
 roof sub-assemblies and from interfacing
 components
– ensuring easy access to fixing components
– ensuring removal and replacement possible
 using labour and tools likely to be available
– ensuring minimal damage to finishes during
 removal and replacement

Design frames so that frame components can
 be separated, permitting replacement of
 only those components which are damaged
Ensure frame materials and sections not over
 specialised, making replacement in later
 years difficult.
Diagram 40 illustrates some of these points:

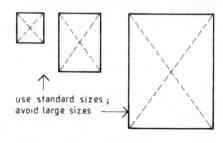

use standard sizes ;
avoid large sizes ⟶

glaze internally if
possible ; use
renewable seals

(a) Glazing

use simple standard components

design profiles which are easy to decorate
and replicate later

(b) Frames

**40**

Another factor is that, wherever possible, components and sub-assemblies
should be designed for upgrading later on. Usually, it is impossible to
foresee what form upgrading will take, but in the case of windows, for

instance, rebates might be designed deep enough to accommodate double-glazing units. Other examples include easily demountable partitions, ceilings, wall panels and floors, increasingly important to commercial and industrial buildings where there are heavy servicing loads, and even structural frames which, suitably designed, can be made to accommodate quite radical alterations in cladding and floor loading.

# 9 Application study 1
# City centre commercial building

In order to exemplify the principles defined and discussed in the previous chapters, it is proposed to describe some aspects of the design and assembly of a typical city centre commercial building, where site constraints play an important role. The areas studied will be the substructure including foundations, the superstructure, assumed to be a steel frame, and the cladding, with additional notes on the buildability aspects of services, finishes and fittings.

Diagram 41 illustrates the general layout of the building at basement, typical floor level and in section:

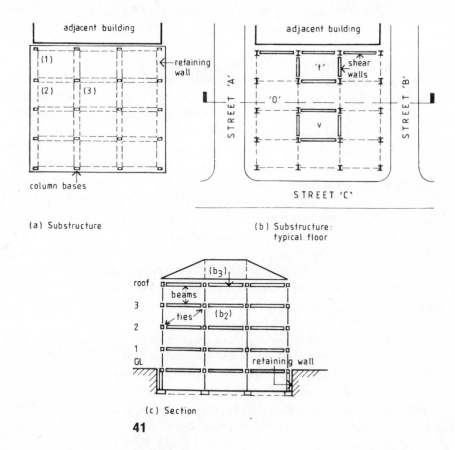

(a) Substructure

(b) Substructure: typical floor

(c) Section

One level of basement, four levels of accommodation above ground level and a roof structure are assumed. The building is surrounded on three sides by streets and abuts another building on the fourth side, with which it shares a party wall. Generally, floors are arranged with a toilet and services' zone 't', a vertical circulation zone 'v' and surrounding open-plan floor space 'o'.


## Substructure

Referring to (a), it can be seen that column bases (1) and (2) interface with the retaining wall, whereas base (3) is freestanding. This immediately raises the problem of whether to:

- continue the steel frame down to foundation level, leading to a possibly complex interface with the retaining wall, unless this is assembled separately from the frame
- design (1) and (2) as part of the retaining wall, possibly in in situ concrete, leaving only the freestanding columns (3) in steelwork
- design (1), (2) and (3) for assembly in in situ concrete, ie the same as the retaining wall, thereby improving buildability by making all assembly processes at this level similar.

Considering these options from the buildability viewpoint, it can be appreciated that separating the basement columns from the retaining wall improves matters, since then they can all be the same and the formwork for the retaining wall becomes simpler. From the structural aspect, however, integrating the columns with the wall improves the stiffness of the wall. It might be preferable to assemble the retaining wall from 'dry' components, such as sheet piles or shaped precast piles, thereby eliminating wet work, but there would be little point in this if all other work below ground level was to be 'wet': once assembly methods had been established for the wall, it would be sensible to apply them to the columns. Better still might be to extend the steel frame down to foundation level, since a major change in assembly method between super- and substructures would be avoided. If this was done, the retaining wall would be separated from the peripheral columns, except for stiffening connections, and would be assembled 'dry' or at least using simple profiles. Diagram 42(a) illustrates this option on plan.

If adopted, this assembly approach might be extended into the design of the foundations themselves, in order to reap maximal buildability benefits. The decision whether to pad or pile would depend upon sub-soil conditions and loading, with choice of type conditioned by such matters as noise, access and plant required as much as by performance. Piling would be particularly difficult on the site shown and for this reason there would

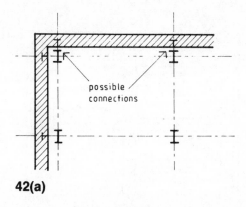

**42(a)**

be a preference for pads, subject to loading and subsoil conditions. This being so, buildability would require a standardisation of pad formwork, both in plan area and depth and, once again, a separation of the pads from the retaining wall. Diagram 42(b) illustrates the desirable conditions in plant and section:

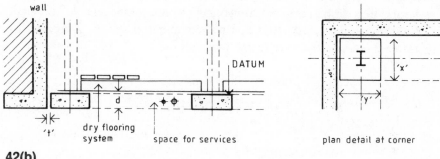

**42(b)**

These solutions represent an ideal, since continuity between pad and retaining wall would probably be essential (at 't'), but at least pads should be square on plan ('x' = 'y'), levelled to ensure proper interfacing with the columns and located accurately in relation to each other and to the steel frame. A further major benefit would follow from this: tie beams '$z_1$' and '$z_2$' could be reduced in variety to two, thereby in turn reducing formwork variety and raising the possibility of using dry, modular units for the basement floor (diagram 42(c)). An alternative method of dealing with the problem of the ground beams would be to excavate for and cast both these and the pads together, thereby simplifying excavation and avoiding disturbance of the pads when preparing for the beams. It would be possible to eliminate excavation for both beams and basement floor slab completely by using steel or precast beams combined with a dry flooring system, possibly of the same type as in the superstructure, thereby further reducing variety and, incidentally, providing space underneath for services (diagram 42(b)).

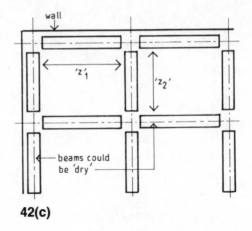

**42(c)**

## Superstructure

The general layout of the superstructure is illustrated in diagram 41. It is assumed to be steel framed, with a cladding of masonry or precast concrete panels (see below). The frame consists of universal stanchions, universal beams and ties, with floors spanning one way onto the beams. A light steel framed roof is supposed, clad in profiled metal sheeting. Diagram 43 illustrates the superstructure frame in greater detail:

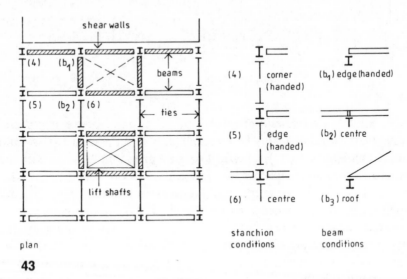

**43**

Beams connect to stanchions in three different ways, (4), (5), (6) and themselves have to satisfy either edge or centre conditions $(b_1)$, $(b_2)$. Smaller beams, or ties, with no responsibility for direct floor loads, connect to stanchions along the other axis and beams at roof level $(b_3)$ (diagram 41(c)) are required to support special roof loads. Shear forces are absorbed by shear walls at the back of the frame and by the boxed lift shafts. Cladding loads are supported by the edge beams and ties.

Good buildability calls for maximal variety reduction and repetition of components and sub-assemblies. The frame described should therefore contain the fewest different types of stanchion, beam and tie and permit the greatest possible ease of assembly. For example, analysing the different stanchion loadings and stresses may suggest many variations in section, both according to disposition on plan and to height in the frame: axial and eccentric loadings will vary for centre, edge and corner conditions and between roof and basement levels. But it may nevertheless be sensible to standardise and limit the variety of sections, both to ease assembly and to make the fabricator's task simpler; one of the disadvantages of computer-aided design is the facility with which sections can be matched to load, resulting in many detailed changes in specification and the unlikelihood of one fabricator being able to supply every section called for. The problem of differing assembly conditions must be faced, however, when it comes to designing the interfacing and fixing components (diagram 43). Connections must be possible both to flanges and webs and, in accordance with buildability principles, these should be achieved by adding or omitting the least variety of different components or materials or by making minimal changes in specification.

Considering the frame as a whole, the sensible division of the building would be into three separate 'lifts', a single-storey one for the basement and two double-height ones for the superstructure, each stanchion of the latter extending through two floors; the roof would be assembled separately. One steelwork section would be specified for the basement, ground and first floors, another for the two upper floors. The fabricator would prepare each stanchion, beam and tie for maximal ease and speed of assembly by welding on seating brackets and plates and drilling holes prior to delivery. Interfacing and fixing components, eg high tensile friction grip (HTFG) bolts, would be standardised throughout. It might be desirable to supply interfacing components pre-fixed to the beams, in order to minimise the difficulty of handling beams into position, care being taken to ensure that beams located at the same height on opposite sides of a stanchion web could be fixed without the need for simultaneous handling; this problem could be overcome if seating brackets were pre-welded to the webs, allowing one beam to 'rest' in position whilst the other was lowered into place (diagram 44(a)). Projecting interfacing components could make crane handling more difficult, since beams could not be slid into position down stanchion webs, but would have to be lowered to one side of the stanchion line, then tilted to clear the flanges. This problem could be solved if stub beams or plates were welded onto the stanchions (diagram 44(b)) and such a solution would be essential if a steel beam positioning manipulator was being used. A final point of importance with the frame

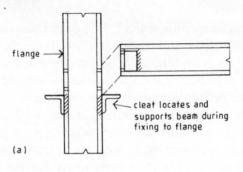

flange →

cleat locates and
supports beam during
fixing to flange

(a)

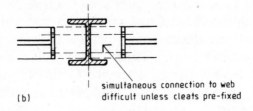

simultaneous connection to web
difficult unless cleats pre-fixed

(b)

**44a**

assembly would be to ensure a proper observation of tolerances, by plumbing and aligning accurately and by providing slotted holes and suitable friction grip washers and shims.

It would be desirable to design a dry assembly floor for the building using, for example, precast or 'composite' construction. Ideally, the stanchion and beam spacings should reflect the modules of the components being used, to avoid cutting or 'specials'. In practice, this is unlikely to be achievable, owing to the many other constraints upon the design. It would be preferable, therefore, to use a 'neutral' system, such as

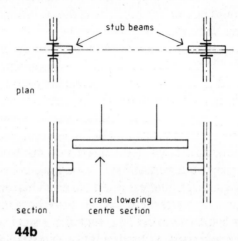

stub beams

plan

section

crane lowering
centre section

**44b**

a ribbed steel deck with lightweight concrete topping, the deck being easy to cut and fit round stanchions and openings. Whichever system is chosen, however, it should obviate the need for supporting formwork and minimise the use of in situ concrete, which would have to be pumped or skip-hoisted to each floor, causing disturbance, mess and delay whilst it dries out. Similar considerations apply to the stanchion and beam fire casings. In situ casing should be avoided and a choice should be made between dry casings and spray-on coatings: the former have the advantage of 'squaring off' the stanchions ready to receive partitions, a job which still has to be done after the spray-on coating has been applied, especially where services have to be concealed. On the other hand, machines are now available which, for simple framed buildings of the type being described, will coat the steelwork automatically 'overnight', thereby reducing disruption and saving on time and labour.

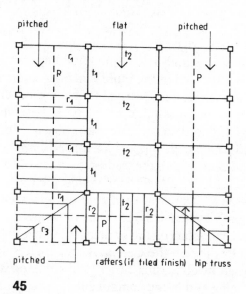

**45**

Diagram 45 illustrates a possible roof design, using light steel half trusses ('$r_1$, $r_2$. $r_3$'), connected by ties ('$t_1$, $t_2$'), supporting purlins ('p'), which in turn support rafters and tiles or a lightweight profiled metal cladding system.

This is a simple approach to the problem, giving three sizes of half truss (which could be reduced to two if the bays were square) and a well-understood, easy to erect cladding method, important in ensuring that the building is enclosed quickly. The trusses would be assembled off-site and lifted into position directly from the delivery vehicle. In this respect, half trusses would be easier to handle than full ones, given the size of the building. One interesting possibility, if there was sufficient space at street level, would be to assemble complete sections of the roof, including trusses, purlins and cladding, prior to lifting, thereby reducing the amount of final assembly needed at roof level and improving its accuracy. Buildability would be further enhanced if the lift motor and tank rooms could be enclosed by the standard roof profile, without the need for vertical projections. Three similar, flat-roofed bays would then give the advantages of repetition and simplicity of design, resulting in less risk of water penetration and failure. At detail design stage, particular attention would have to be paid to the roof's interfacing and fixing components and to such secondary components as gutters, channels and downpipes. Again, the usual buildability principles would apply: standard, tested components universally applied and easily assembled using simple tools, competent labour and the least amount and complexity of temporary work.

## Cladding

Cladding has to meet rigorous function and performance criteria, especially in a medium- or high-rise framed building, but is also sensitive to buildability. For example, in the building being studied, the cladding must be fixable to the steel frame, be capable of being assembled rapidly to minimise exposure to the weather and, ideally, be assemblable from the interior to obviate the need for scaffolding. Once assembled, it should provide secure and convenient support for finishes, fittings and services. The structural conditions which the cladding system must satisfy include interfacing with stanchions on their flange sides, their web sides and with both sides at the corners. The problem of interfacing is complicated by the need to fire case both stanchions and beams and by the desirability of supporting the cladding solely on the stanchions, rather than on the beams and ties: the extra loading on these components might require different, heavier sections, thereby increasing variety and reducing standardisation. Ideally, the interfacing and fixing components for the cladding would be similar to those for the beams and ties, in the sense that special cleats, plates or holes would not be required.

The requirements for a cladding system can be summarised as follows:
– modular in relation to frame and each sub-assembly; ideally, of bay width and height;
– minimal differences between units, regardless of location in the building (diagram 12);
– transportable on a standard delivery vehicle;
– fixable direct from the delivery vehicle;
– require minimal temporary works to assemble in position;
– require minimal specialised labour, tools, plant and equipment;
– fixing to take place in the least hostile environment.

Of the three main contenders for the building being considered, masonry, precast concrete and lightweight frame and panel, precast concrete appears to offer the balance of advantages, since panels can be designed to satisfy all the above criteria and to suffer relatively few disadvantages. For example, whereas masonry panels must be built up from small units, which must be stored, lifted laboriously into position and assembled from an external scaffold, precast panels can be lifted from the delivery vehicle and placed in one operation. Similarly, lightweight framed systems consist of large numbers of separate and precisely fabricated small components, which are difficult to assemble accurately in adverse weather conditions from an often cramped scaffold and which are therefore best sub-assembled at ground level. Unfortunately, this requires space, which may not be available on a crowded site, and extreme care when hoisting into position, especially where scaffolding obstructs access to the building face; specialised labour and tools may also be needed. Some of these objections can be levelled at precast panels. For example, where external fixing or the insertion of weather seals or mastic are required, scaffolding will be necessary and this can obstruct handling (diagram 36), but, given suitable design, scaffolding can be eliminated and all assembly carried out from the interior of the building. One way of achieving this objective is illustrated in diagram 46:

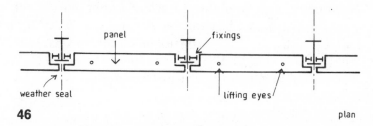

**46**                                                                        plan

Panels are handled into position and fixed to stanchions using plates either pre-assembled to the panels or inserted between panel and stanchion as the former rests upon the tie; pre-welding the plates to the stanchions prior to frame erection would create stanchion 'specials', adversely affecting handling precedence. Unfortunately, this solution would not resolve the problem of fixing weather seals and mastic between the panel ends. To do this, either panels would have to be designed to make the internal fixing of weather seals possible, for example by arranging for end-to-end and horizontal joints to occur between stanchions, or insertion could be from gantries suspended from the roof structure. The internal fixing of glazing is a simple matter and this is desirable anyway to ensure good buildability in use. Other problems to be overcome include ensuring that panels will either weather evenly or can be cleaned economically and that the relationship between the weather skin and internal linings and finishes has been properly considered. Diagram 47 illustrates schematically the general sequence of assembly:

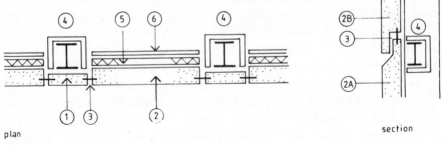

plan

section

**47**

A short section of cladding (1) is assembled to the stanchion flange or web, followed by the main cladding panel (2), this also being assembled to the stanchion using appropriate interfacing and fixing components; the weather seals (3) are inserted from inside the building; dry fire casings (4) are secured to the stanchions, these then defining the spaces between stanchions which must be filled with insulation (5) and finishing components (6). Panels are assembled in sequence up the building face, floor by floor, employing a suitable design of overlapping joint (section (2A), (2B)). Many variations of this method of assembly are possible, but the general principle should be clear: buildability is a matter of thinking clearly and practically about the sequence of assembly of components, so that assembly can proceed smoothly without compromising the other design objectives of function, performance and aesthetics.

**Services, finishes and fittings**
As more and more components and sub-assemblies are added to the building, their interrelationships become increasingly complex, with many implications for buildability. Both frame and cladding affect the sequence and method of assembly of the services and all three influence the choice and assembly method of the finishes and fittings. For instance, rainwater run-off begins as soon as the roof finish is complete and, although there is protection of the interior of the building, water is concentrated at points on the roof edges and can affect assembly of the cladding. For this reason, early installation of either temporary or permanent gutters and downpipes, together with the associated drainage, is important. The ideal sequence for the building being considered is, therefore:
roof structure → weather sheeting → gutters and downpipes → cladding.

It follows that the gutters and downpipes should not depend upon the cladding for support and downpipes will therefore have to be secured to the frame. This can cause problems, however: downpipes are often of substantial size if draining large areas of roof and specified in cast iron, resulting in inflexibility and difficulty in handling and assembling. For these reasons, routes down the structure must be carefully planned, especially where beams obstruct the direct vertical line, and holes and ducts formed accurately.

As a general principle, first-fix or carcassing of services should commence as soon as structural floors, including any toppings, are complete. It is a waste of time to wait for completion of the cladding and this is a further reason for selecting a cladding type which can be assembled rapidly and for allowing the structural floors to support all carcassing loads. Furthermore, carcassing pipework and trunking should be attached to the underside of the structural floor, rather than be supported on top of it, since any obstruction of the floor surface will impede horizontal transfer. The preferred order of assembly of services is as follows:

- rainwater gutters and downpipes;
- screwed steel pipework and cast-iron risers, eg for sprinklers;
- trunking;
- second-fix pipework, copper plumbing, etc;
- electrical and communications distribution;
- fittings and terminals.

Once the downpipes have been installed, the screwed steel pipework, for sprinkler and heating systems for example, can be attached to the underside of the floor. This process is greatly assisted if easy fixing to the floor soffit is possible, as it is with some types of steel composite floor deck, and if brackets and hangers have been accurately located and are easily adjustable. It is also essential that any vertical and horizontal ducts required to support risers and distribution mains have been assembled by this stage. The preferred sequence of assembly is shown in diagram 48:

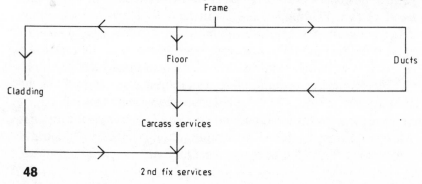

48

Since assembly of ducts and structural floor should proceed simult-aneously, with cladding following immediately afterwards, designers should consider the possibility of at least partially integrating these sub-assemblies, for example by developing edge beams which are deep enough to form spandrel panels (despite variety increase) or ducts which form part of the shear walls and lift shaft boxes. As far as the pipework itself is concerned, assembly can proceed rapidly if pipe sections are modular, do not have to be routed round downstand beams and stanchions and are easily accessible. To this end, floor to floor heights should be calculated to permit steel pipework and trunking to run below beams, that is where beams cannot be eliminated through appropriate design of the structural floor.

Similar considerations apply to the installation of trunking. Since this is bulky, careful routing is even more important, with the largest sections nearest the ducts kept clear of beams, or at least occupying spaces where reduced headroom is acceptable. Modular sections can reduce the need for cutting on site and care must be taken to ensure the proper provision of suspension brackets and hangers. Since the units are large, they can obstruct access to previously fixed pipework and this should be allowed for in design to ensure both simple initial assembly and good buildability in use.

Carcassing of electrical and communications services usually requires the assembly of at least the 'weather' skin of the cladding, but it can be a two-stage process. Preliminary work requires the fixing of cable trays and hangers, which must be located in relation to pipework, trunking and partition lines so as to ensure access when it comes to second-fix stage. Vertical routes through the structural floor may be necessary to connect mains to the network of cables which will occupy the 'access' floor zone and openings should be pre-planned to avoid last minute drilling.

Some second-fix pipework, for example copper plumbing and connec-tions to sprinkler heads, can be assembled at a relatively early stage, although fixing the latter may depend upon the assembly of the suspended ceiling grid. The majority, however, must await assembly of partitions and completion of the cladding. There is, in fact, such an intimate inter-dependence between these two sub-assemblies and the services at second-fix stage, that a clear understanding by the designer of the relationships is essential. This is well illustrated by the assembly of metal stud partition-ing: a density of services at ceiling level can inhibit easy assembly of the partition frame, which must be threaded round pipes and trunking, whilst maintaining as far as possible its modular characteristics. Once the frame is complete, one side may be lined before pipe and cable drops are added and secured to purpose-located timber battens. Only then can the other side be lined and holes formed for the later addition of terminals and switch plates. The necessary close interdependency of the trades will be apparent. Second-fixing to the cladding depends usually upon the completion of the weather skin and the insulation, but must precede the addition of linings and decorative finishes.

Final fitting out depends upon a dry, clean interior, with clear access to floors, walls and ceilings. It is hard to define an optimal sequence of assembly, since there is a continuing close interdependency between components and sub-assemblies and many activities can take place in parallel. For example, partitions may extend above the level of the suspended ceiling to prevent the passage between rooms of flame, smoke and noise, and this requires almost simultaneous assembly of the two elements; the interrelationship between partition erectors, plumbers and electricians has already been referred to; problem areas, such as the junctions between walls and ceilings and between surface finishes, such as tiling, and fittings and electrical outlets and switch plates, require particular attention. The satisfactory resolution of such difficulties is important, however, if good buildability and a high quality of internal finish are to be achieved.

### Labour, tools, plant and equipment
Good buildability requires proper attention to be paid not only to such matters as tolerances, variety reduction and repetition and the efficient conversion of materials to components and sub-assemblies, but also to the optimal deployment of the labour force and the choice of the most appropriate tools, plant and equipment. The building chosen for this study occupies a city centre site bounded by streets and an adjoining building (diagram 41). The problems for management, therefore, include how to eliminate as far as possible specialist labour and plant, so as to simplify and speed assembly, where to offload and store materials, components and sub-asemblies during the various stages of the work and where to locate major fixed plant such as a tower crane. Temporary works, such as site offices and scaffolding, also require careful selection, location and programming for erection and dismantling.

A number of possible solutions have already been proposed. For example, by continuing the steel frame down to basement level, the variety of different structural systems can be reduced and by detailed attention to the design of the steel frame and in particular to its interfaces with the cladding, column and beam variations can also be minimised. Such simplification will have a beneficial effect upon labour type and quality. Once the piles or pads, retaining walls and basement floor slab have been driven or cast, steel erectors can take over and complete the whole of the frame, including the roof structure, thereby reaping the benefits of repetitive working. Similarly, a single system of cladding makes it possible to complete that sub-assembly rapidly, as do the use of beam casings and partitioning systems which can be carried out by one trade, for example the plasterers. Specialist work cannot be avoided for the services' installations, but careful design here, in such areas as frame/cladding interrelationships and the sequencing of installation, will pay dividends.

Matters are not so straightforward in the matter of plant and temporary works, since the tight constraints of the site make choice and location a difficult decision. For example (diagram 41), it may be necessary to close Street 'B' during most of the assembly period to allow for delivery, off-loading and storage of materials and components. The fixed crane must be placed where it can cover the whole site without unduly overswinging adjacent buildings and streets and where maximal control of handling can be achieved, and this may mean it also being in Street 'B', unless a climbing type is chosen or it is located internally. In any case it will probably be necessary to replace it as quickly as possible with a hoist, supplemented by a mobile crane, and as this change will occur once the building has been enclosed, a further stimulus is given to the rapid completion of frame and cladding.

Where the pre-assembly of large sub-assemblies, or the delivery and storage of relatively large sub-assemblies such as boiler and air handling equipment, is proposed spaces must be made available for this work to be carried out and, again, the only clear option on the site in question is the street. For example, the choice of cladding referred to earlier must take this factor into account, in that, whereas lifting and placing direct from the delivery vehicle is possible with precast units, this is not the case with lightweight systems containing many small components. Accurate delivery scheduling, to minimise storage and reduce vehicle turn-round time, is therefore important, as is the making up of loads to ensure that the correct handling sequence can be maintained. Generally, design should seek to minimise the length of time deliveries, storage and handling obstruct traffic routes, both by adopting the strategy described for large components and by ensuring that smaller components can be moved rapidly into the building interior and stored near workplaces. Where a degree of obstuction over quite a long period is unavoidable, as with concrete delivery, off-loading bays recessed into the street frontage should be contrived.

A final point to be considered in the building being studied are the type and location of temporary works and particularly of the scaffolding. Scaffolding can obstruct not only pavements but also access to the building during assembly. Designers should, therefore, envisage assembly from the building interior as far as possible – this is suggested earlier in the cladding study – and where impossible, as with roof weather sheeting and edge trims and external pointing and cleaning, consider the use of alternatives such as gantries, hanging scaffolds and mobile cranes.

Since scaffolding towers, permitting the use of cranes once the building is enclosed, would cause too much obstruction at street level, the use of hoists becomes unavoidable. Their location should be carefully considered, since most can not handle bulky loads and can obstruct final completion of the cladding. At some point, therefore, vertical transfer handling will have to move to the interior, to the lifts perhaps, to allow dismantling of the hoist to take place. This, however, places responsibility upon the lift installers to complete their work on time and in coordination with, for example, the work of services' second-fixers and decorators.

Overall, so interdependent are plant, temporary works and design, that designers and constructors have a prime responsibility to understand each other's requirements from the earliest design stages, especially where, as in this case, the constraints of the site are such a major factor in achieving good buildability.

# 10 Application study 2 Private housing development

The commonest form of building universally is the dwelling, either on its own as the individual house, or arranged in groups, in the form of houses, flats or maisonettes. This Study considers both the individual house and the housing layout from the buildability point of view, demonstrating that even such an apparently uncomplicated building type can be affected markedly by assembly sequences and processes.

The Study divides into two parts, the layout and the house itself (a house, rather than a flat or maisonette will be considered). Diagram 49 illustrates a layout of moderate size, such as might be found in the outer suburbs of a fair sized town. Existing streets bound two sides (East Street, East Lane and South Street) and new boundaries to open country the other two. New access roads 1 and 2 have been approved, as has the improvement of East Lane by widening, straightening and the provision of a footpath. The site contains no natural features, other than an even and gentle slope from west to east, and the subsoil is uncomplicated and of good bearing quality.

## LAYOUT: buildability factors

The layout was designed without particular concern for buildability principles. Those which are of particular importance in layout design are as follows:
- good access to the site for delivery vehicles;
- offices, storage compounds and workshops related to the delivery point;
- a through route for delivery vehicles if possible;
- minimal need for temporary accesses to buildings being assembled;
- geometrically comprehensible relationships between buildings to assist setting out;
- minimal obstruction to layouts by sewers, underground workings, waterlogged or polluted ground, preserved trees, overhead cables, adjacent buildings, etc;
- best possible integration of roads, sewers, drains and main services;
- individual sites to be as level as possible;
- top-soil storage areas which minimise carting distances.

## Good access for vehicles

The issues affecting site buildability are discussed in chapter 2. Poor access to the site has the following main disadvantages: the sizes and types of delivery vehicles, and of the loads which they carry, are limited; there may be interference with traffic on the public highway; accesses may be so awkwardly positioned that they interfere with manoevrability on the site itself. Furthermore, after the vehicles have entered the site, loads must either be off-loaded into central or satellite storage areas, or delivered direct to the buildings currently being assembled, and such storage areas and off-loading points may not be accessible if, for example, poor phasing of the work on sewers, main services and road bases has resulted in their not being completed ahead of the main contract. On the site illustrated, assuming an order of build which follows the numbering of the blocks, it is essential to have completed the access from South Street, a section of New Road 1 and the whole of New Road 2 up to base course level if work on blocks 1–6 is to proceed smoothly, and 'completion' includes not only the sewering and services' installations mentioned, but also the possible provisions of a turning head at the end of New Road 2 suitable for large vehicles.

## Offices, storage compounds and workshops related to the delivery point

In the scheme illustrated, the decision has been taken to establish the main storage area and the site offices at the South Street access point, with stores and workshops to the left and offices to the right. Owing to the location of block 1 and the line of New Road 2, this means that the compound becomes long and narrow, making access and vehicles manoevring within it difficult. The problem can be overcome if a second exit is provided where shown, allowing one way working, a further reason for constructing New Road 2 early in the contract. It is still necessary, however, to ensure proper control and checking of vehicles entering and leaving the site and a check-point will have to be located where shown until New Road 1 is driven through, when dual accesses will complicate matters. Note that the separation of the offices from the compound makes control difficult, since vehicles entering and leaving the latter are not subject to visual control from a cabin and that, once the most distant parts of the site are opened up, at blocks 10–14, control will become even harder and it may be necessary to establish a secondary storage and compound area at the northern entrance to New Road 1. This problem should be considered together with that of the order of site completion: not shown in diagram 49 are blocks 19–21, which occupy the area of the offices and the compounds and which face onto South Street; site management must consider when to dismantle the temporary accommodation and whether to remove it completely or to relocate it in a position convenient for the assembly of these last three blocks.

**Provide through accesses for delivery vehicles**

In addition to the observations already made about the construction of New Road 1 and the provision of a secondary exit from the compound, it is important to emphasise that new road and temporary access construction should take account of the difficulty caused if large, heavily-laden vehicles and plant have to manoeuvre in a limited space on poorly compacted or muddy ground. For example, once blocks 1–6 are finished, it will be necessary to gain access to blocks 7–12 and New Road 1 will therefore have to be completed in good time, as will the temporary access shown. Note, however, that whereas the former is a through route, the latter is a dead end and that it would be desirable to connect it to the head of New Road 2 during construction, accepting the loss until later in the contract of one unit from the end of block 6. This is a decision which will have to be taken during the layout design stage and in cooperation between designer and constructor. The advantage to vehicles and plant if this alteration were to be approved will be apparent.

**Minimal need for temporary accesses**

Temporary accesses are expensive, waste time in constructing and removing and occupy space on site. The reasons for providing them include roads' contracts which are not complete before building work begins, permanent roads which are too far from buildings, temporary works such as scaffolding which obstruct routes between buildings, superstructure assembly methods which require a close approach by plant and the obstruction of permanent roads by building operations. In the layout illustrated, all blocks except numbers 10 and 11 are reasonably accessible, assuming conventional masonry construction, although 'stub' accesses may be necessary for numbers 1–4, 12 and 14. The solutions to the problems are mainly self-evident and can, for the most part, be accommodated during design. For example, almost all dwellings will require parking or garaging close beside them, in other words permanent road access, and the location of drives and forecourts should, where possible, reflect the needs of construction vehicles as well as of the ultimate users. Where this is not possible, as with blocks 10 and 11, a temporary access may have to be provided, but if this can give access to a garage court, for example, the expense will have been justified. The need for temporary accesses can be minimised, if not eliminated altogether, by observing the following principles:

– complete permanent roads to base course level before the main contract begins;

- design roads and accesses for dual use by construction vehicles and ultimate users;
- select plant for major assembly stages which can work 'across' the building being assembled from one side, eg the mini-tower crane;
- design spaces between blocks to allow access from one side to the other, even when scaffolding has been erected;
- design scaffolding and select plant which enable materials, components and sub-assemblies to be hoisted to one point, then moved round or across the building to the workplace without further changes in level;
- plan building operations so that permanent roads will not be obstructed.

**Set out buildings according to geometrically comprehensible relationships**

The problems which arise at setting out stage when buildings are scattered 'at random' across a site are discussed in chapter 7(e). Buildability is improved if buildings can be plotted in relation to the roads, and the roads to the site, speedily and accurately and it can be seen on diagram 49 that this will not be possible with all the housing blocks. For example, whereas numbers 1–6 are set out at right angles to each other, with numbers 2 and 3 touching the back of the footpath and 1 and 4 aligned with their gable ends, numbers 7, 8 and 9 have complex inter-relationships, both with each other and with the road which curves in front of them. Numbers 10 and 16 are likely to cause similar, if lesser, difficulties. Since setting out is further complicated by the addition of sewer and service lines and levels, the greatest degree of simplicity, consistent with design quality, should be sought. To summarise the basic principles:

- buildings should be set out in relation to the National Grid Reference; for preference, whole angular and linear units of measurements should be chosen;
- building forms should be simple, with minimal changes in direction of walls; where changes do occur, they should avoid complex angles and curves;
- curves, especially of roads and paths, should be struck from the fewest possible number of centres and the centres themselves should be related comprehensibly to each other;
- levels should be simple to measure and there should be the fewest number of level changes, especially within the same building or block: this precept is likely to affect blocks 5, 11 and 12 in the layout being studied;
- sufficient fixed, accurate references should be established during initial setting out of the site to prevent cumulative errors building up, a matter of surveying technique;
- last minute changes in layout and building design should be avoided.

**Minimal obstructions to layouts by sewers, underground workings, poor ground, trees, overhead obstructions, etc:**
Obstructions on site can affect the planning of buildings, roads and services and also prevent or inhibit the use of certain types of plant. The importance of accurate survey information cannot be overemphasised, therefore, especially of possible obstructions below ground. On diagram 49, it will be noted that a number of problems have been revealed, especially at the north end of the site, which will affect the layout. For example, borehole surveys have revealed areas of poor ground and an old mine shaft, there is a line of sewers running across the site from west to east and the topographical survey has recorded a line of overhead cables cutting off the topmost corner. Meanwhile, the realignment and widening of East Lane must take account of an avenue of mature trees, upon which a Tree Preservation Order has been served. The result of all this will be the need for realignment of at least some of the blocks, for example 10 and 13, and a probable loss of others, such as 11 and 12. Since the effect of such a loss upon scheme viability may be significant, early knowledge is vital. Not that all is lost, however: it may be possible to have the overhead cables realigned clear of the site and the poor ground cut out or consolidated. Even if building is not possible, some other use may be found for the affected area of ground, for example as recreation or play space, which will add to the attractiveness and hence commercial viability of the scheme as a whole.

**Achieve the best possible integration of roads, sewers, main services and drains**
Attention to this point follows naturally from what is stated above. The essential strategy is to ensure that roads, sewers and main services are completed before building begins, at least to the extent of the formation of road bases and the laying of sewers, ducts for service pipes and cables where they underlie roads, since such work is highly disruptive once building has started.

On the site in question, assuming the phasing suggested earlier, work on New Road 2, together with its associated drains and services, must be completed first, followed by that to New Road 1 and, finally, to East Lane. Quite often, integration of roads' and services' contracts can cause difficulty, since the different companies may find it hard to coordinate their activities and especially their timing. It is possible to mitigate the worst effects of this, however, by reducing the dependence of one part upon another. For example, although roads are dependent upon sewers when the latter run under the former, it may be possible to separate the two. Thus, in diagram 49, a possible sewer line lies down the divide between blocks 6 and 7–9, sewers here serving those blocks and possibly, by a spur,

Materials delivered to the blocks under construction :

| | |
|---|---|
| bricks | ✳ plasters |
| blocks | ✳ screeding materials |
| roof tiles | ✳ manufactured joinery |
| roof trusses | |
| joists | ✳ inside completed shell |

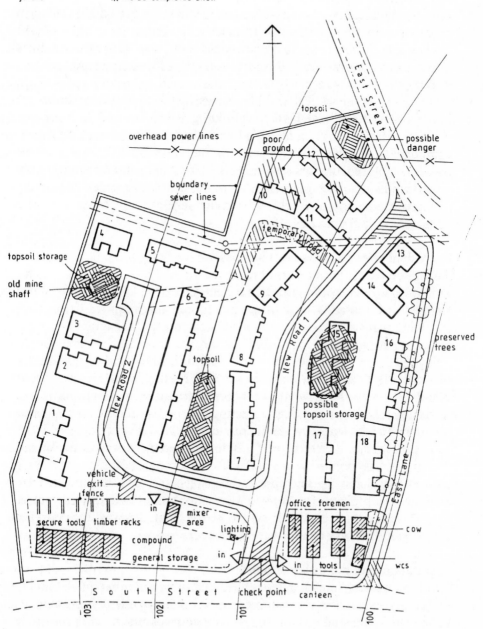

blocks 4 and 5, the final connection being made to the existing sewers shown at the north end. A separate, short, sewer could serve blocks 1–3 and connect at its south end into the existing sewer in South Street. By this device, no sewers at all need underlie New Road 2 and if a similar approach was followed between blocks 15–18, New Road 1 could also be freed of interdependence, except at its north end. Main services could be treated in a similar way, their routing being related to verges, footpaths and soft landscaping, it being essential in this case to incorporate cross-road ducts in the roads' contract and to complete them before temporary accesses, buildings or temporary works are constructed or before spoil heaps accumulate. At the tactical level of services' installation, it is important for house drains to be laid before scaffolding is erected and to speed the process of drainlaying, rapid assembly methods, using modern materials, components and jointing systems, should be adopted. Similarly, the excavation of trenches for services between buildings and the main supply lines should not take place late in the assembly sequence, when the finishing trades are at work and require level, clean access for easily damaged components.

### Individual sites to be as level as possible

The more level the site, the better the buildability. For this reason, building across contours should be minimised, since, although sites can be stepped and regraded by cutting and filling, this requires extra work involving plant and, usually, retaining structures. On diagram 49, it can be seen that, with contours running from north to south, blocks should likewise run in these directions and that difficulties will be caused for blocks 5, 10–12 and 19–21 (not shown, but fronting South Street). Blocks 4 and 14, being short, would probably not require anything but minor terracing. The other problems affecting blocks 10–12 have already been mentioned and it would appear increasingly advisable to omit these blocks from the scheme altogether, or at least to redesign them drastically. Where running across contours is unavoidable, for reasons of planning, it is better to split the blocks up into shorter units of one or two houses, thereby avoiding the problems of stepped foundations and complex junctions at roof level (diagram 50). Block 5 could be treated in this way, for example, at the point half way along where it 'staggers' on plan.

### Maintain a rational order of build

It will be evident from all that has been said previously that buildability is served best when assembly proceeds in a rational manner. For example, on the site being studied, it is supposed that development will proceed in the order of block numbering and that this will dictate the order of letting of roads', services' and buildings' contracts as well as the strategy for siting of compounds, offices and spoil heaps. The supposition may not be correct, however, if the development is of houses for private sale and if marketing strategy dictates that the houses fronting South Street or East Lane are built and sold first. Another consideration is whether to develop on 'out from end of cul-de-sac' or 'in from main access' principles, this problem occurring with New Road 2: the advantage of working 'in' for the constructor will be offset by the disadvantages, in terms of mess and disruption, for the first occupiers of the completed houses.

**Reduce carting distances to top-soil storage areas**
A final, but important, point in the buildability of layout design concerns travel distances by plant during site clearance and 'reducing levels' stages. Top soil is reused for gardens and soft landscaping, the majority being retained on site close, ideally, to where it will be required later on. Diagram 49 illustrates possible locations for these spoil heaps and a number of points need to be made about them:

– excessive carting distances should be avoided, but this principle will be hard to observe in the cases of blocks 13–19; the order of build must therefore take account of this factor, perhaps by stockpiling in the area of block 15 and completing this block as one of the last, once the soil has been distributed to already completed gardens;
– one of the undesirable effects of long carting distances, apart from loss of time, is undue compaction or breaking up of the soil, making subsequent building operations more difficult. This problem can be mitigated by choice of route and correct selection of plant, with the right combination of capacity, drive method and tyring;
– heaps should not be so large or so steeply graded that they become waterlogged and dangerous (the one adjacent to block 12 is too close to East Street); it is better to have several small heaps evenly distributed than one, centrally placed, large one;
– areas of poor ground or old mine shafts can be chosen for stockpiling, since they may not be built on (one such area is shown between blocks 3 and 4), provided that there is sufficient strength in the caps to support the loads, both of material and of the machines working it;
– on tightly planned sites, or on sites poorly provided with top soil, it may have to be imported; in this event, temporary storage may be necessary and space must be set aside for it;
– it may be necessary, sometimes, to retain a proportion of the subsoil, perhaps where regrading has been carried out or for backfilling behind retaining walls; since this must be kept separate from the topsoil, separate storage areas should be provided.

## DWELLINGS: buildability considerations

The scheme illustrated in diagram 49 is of a development of predominantly terraced dwellings for low cost sale or rent. Although no particular unit is defined clearly, it will be apparent that there is a wide range of types, of varying frontages and depths, with plan forms which differ markedly. The blocks have complex relationships to each other, as has already been pointed out, and within several of the blocks there is stepping and staggering in section and plan. None of these features suggests that buildability will be good, since the cardinal principles of variety reduction and repetition are not being observed. To demonstrate the applicability of buildability principles to large scale, high density housing developments of this type, observations will be made under the following headings:
– foundations and substructure;
– superstructure;
– services;
– finishes and fittings.

### Foundations and substructure

Since it is supposed that the subsoil is uncomplicated and of good bearing quality (except where indicated on the layout plan), the usual options of wide strip, trench fill, raft or short-bore piling will be open to the designer. The decision which to use will depend partly upon the complexity of the plan form, partly on the subsoil conditions in relation to loadings and stability, and partly upon the ability of the constructor and the availability to him of suitable materials, labour and plant. For example, block 1 has a complex plan form with no level changes, which is likely to need expensive formwork if the decision is to raft, whereas block 6 is well suited to long strip casting, since sides are straight (the porches can be founded separately) and the floor is level. Blocks 2, 3 and 5, on the other hand, may require stepping at some point in their length as well as the forming of projections on plan, whereas blocks 10–12, if they are to be built at all for reasons given earlier, may require special foundations, or at least prior consolidation of the subsoil. The point is made: by redesigning the scheme in relatively minor respects, little quality will be lost and much buildability gained.

Diagram 50(a) shows in outline the various dwelling types which make up the scheme (all assumed to be houses), with types (i) and (ii) predominating and being used in various combinations of handing and terracing in blocks 2–12, 16–18 and 19–21 (not shown). Unfortunately, the designer has chosen completely different plan forms for blocks 1, 13 and 14 and has staggered the terrace of four units of type (i) in block 15. He has also introduced minor, but probably insignificant, variations in blocks 5

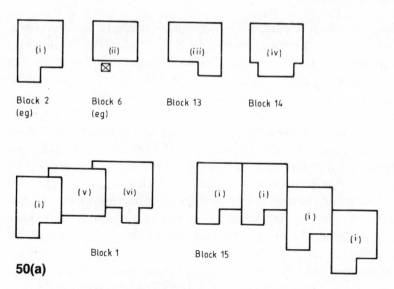

**50(a)**

and 7 (staggering and additional 'lean-tos'). It would greatly assist the constructor if the major variations at least could be eliminated and diagram 50(b) shows how this might be done:

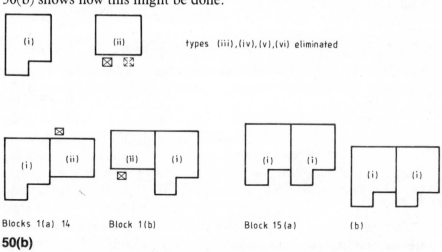

**50(b)**

'One-off' types, used only in blocks 13 and 14, are eliminated completely, houses here being either of type (i) (block 13) or of a new type combining types (i) and (ii), block 1 having been rearranged into two separate parts, each of which contains this new type; in other words, the whole scheme can now be built up from only two plan variations, offering major advantages in variety reduction and repetition. Note, incidentally, that block 15 has been simplified and split into two parts, thereby reducing the amount of staggering, the only suspect point to watch here being the closeness of the trenching at the adjacent gables, which may present difficulties to the digger operator – a problem eliminated if rafting is used. Further worthwhile simplifications to the scheme would be the omission of minor staggers, as in blocks 5 and 7, and of randomly placed lean-tos (block 7), although by designing the 'porch' in the type (ii) to be assembled separately from the main building, it could be used anywhere allowable by the plan.

The amendments proposed for the purpose of simplifying the layout will, of course, assist assembly of both sub- and superstructures. Trench fill will be the normal choice of foundation for housing of this type, since excavation and concreting are economical activities and require no elaborate formwork, reinforcement, or control of concrete quality. On the other hand, by simplifying the layout, economical reuse of formwork becomes possible and rafting will be a positive advantage in areas of poor ground, such as in the vicinity of blocks 10–12. The final decision may depend upon the plan forms and in particular upon the location of loadbearing walls. For example, in the type (i) plan (diagram 51), an internal loadbearing wall is required where shown, since the span between cross-walls would otherwise be too great:

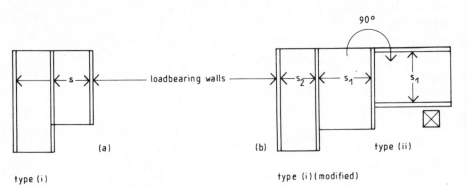

(a)    loadbearing walls    (b)    type (ii)

type (i)    type (i)(modified)

**51**

This still leaves the choice of foundation open, but the designs of both ground and first floor sub-assemblies will be greatly influenced by the types selected. For, assuming strip footings, the normal choice for the ground floor will be either in situ concrete or precast beams and pots and for the first floor, timber joists. The span 'S' will, therefore, have to be within the structural limits for these components. Furthermore, as is shown in diagram 51(b), buildability of both types (i) and (ii) can be usefully enhanced if the spans side to side and front to back are made the same, with only '$S_2$' differing in the interests of plan variability. It would even be possible, by rotating the larger part of the type (i) plan through 90°, to use that part for the type (ii) plan, assuming that loadbearing walls running in the opposite direction were acceptable.

## Superstructure

For the purposes of this study, it is assumed that the materials, components and sub-assemblies comprising the superstructure are conventional, that is consist of bricks, blocks, timber joists and trusses, with all the interfacing and fixing components necessary to enable these primary components to be assembled. Within this vocabulary, however, certain choices and decisions affecting buildability are possible and these will be discussed under the headings of the major sub-assemblies of walls, floors and roofs, with further reference to major openings in the fabric – windows and doors.

**Walls**   It is of assistance to the bricklayer if walls are kept simple, both in plan and section and this is one of the reasons why the alterations illustrated in diagram 50 were proposed: the original complexity of block 1, for example, would have meant careful setting out and delays whilst changes of direction and varying wall lengths were measured and built. Although the proposed amendment (diagram 50(b)) is still relatively complex, once it has been learnt it can be applied elsewhere in the schemes, in block 14 for example, thereby speeding up the work and improving quality. Similarly, the division of blocks 1 and 15 into pairs of semi-detached dwellings enables relatively simple gable brickwork to be erected, again on a repeating pattern, compared with the complexities of party wall assembly which would arise with the earlier proposals. This simplification has its effect in section also: with pitched roofs, difficult to assemble interfaces would occur in the original block 1 where roofs of adjacent dwellings meet and have to be supported on party walls. The problem is illustrated in diagram 52:

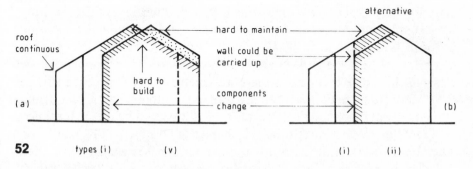

**52**        types (i)            (v)                              (i)      (ii)

In (a), the original proposal, difficulties arise at the points indicated, caused by the staggering of the dwellings and their overlapping along the back elevation. Not only will tiling and flashing cause problems, but it will also be necessary to change components along the line of the party wall from blocks to bricks, a well understood practice but one, nevertheless, which increases complication and causes delay. The amendment proposed is shown in (b): here, although the type (ii) is set back, it shares a common rear elevation with the type (i) and even, partly, a common roof surface. Although a change of component in the party wall is still necessary in the shaded area, even this could be eliminated by continuing the front elevation of the type (ii) up to meet the roof line of the type (i). This would also remove the hard to maintain area of the upper wall. Note that the projection to the side of the type (i) is dealt with by carrying the roof down over it, thereby simplifying assembly of both roof structure and finishes (assuming that the plan can accommodate this roof form). One further point should be made about the assembly of dwellings in terraces: the complications of component changes and flashings at party wall interfaces occur also when dwellings are stepped down slopes, the problem being exacerbated further by foundations and floors which intersect the walls at differing levels. It is desirable, therefore, to separate dwellings at points of stepping, as in diagram 50(b), and at all costs to avoid the extreme complication of both stepping and staggering continuous lines of dwellings: the problems presented may intrigue both designer and constructor, but the sometimes ingenious solutions found will certainly be at the client's expense.

**Floors**   The potential for simplification of the floor structure has already been referred to and illustrated (diagram 51). The extreme simplification proposed, whereby the type (ii) plan is but the type (i) rotated through 90°, may not be justified for planning reasons, and is in any case of less moment where the structure is timber joists, which may be supplied to any length, rather than precast beams or planks. There is a further consideration however: where chipboard or plywood and plasterboard sheets are being used for floor decks and ceilings, the internal dimensions of the dwelling shell should reflect those sheet modules, to minimise the amount of cutting to waste. Not that this can be taken too far: bricklayers work to less precise tolerances than woodworkers and a shell accurately dimensioned by the designer to utilise every last square millimetre of chipboard can still be 10–25 mm out, or even out of 'square', when assembled, thereby requiring difficult to cut strips and feathering to fill in the gaps. The reason for this is inherent 'tolerance incompatibility' (chapter 1 and appendix 1), which can only be avoided, either by insisting upon precise working from the bricklayer, or by selecting a superstructure system, such as timber panel, in which the necessary finer tolerances are inherent. In practical terms, therefore, where tolerance incompatibility is unavoidable, it is better to allow a certain amount of oversizing when calculating sheet modules, or to design for overlaps or masking by other components so that overwide joints can be concealed (diagram 54).

**Roofs** In the scheme being studied, conventional pitched roofs are assumed and the arguments for rationalisation of the dwelling shells is given further force by the fact that trussed rafters, the still almost inevitable choice on cost grounds, are components fabricated off-site under factory conditions. It is essential, therefore, to minimise variety and maximise repetition in order to reduce the costs of components and labour to a minimum. Referring to diagrams 50, 51 and 52, however, it can be seen that the argument about roof rationalisation is different from that about the floors: for reasons discussed above ('Walls'), the ridge lines are made discontinuous through types (i) and (ii) where these abut, although the roof pitch is the same, this in order that part of the roof surface can be shared (diagram 52). Two types of truss are required, therefore, of similar pitch but different span, with an extension to the upper chord of the type (i) truss where it extends over the plan projection. Nevertheless, given the other amendments proposed for the layout as a whole, only two basic truss types will be needed for the entire scheme, a great advantage. For planning reasons, such as the provision of living space in the roof, an alternative roof structure might be chosen, for example purlin and rafter or 'attic truss'. In the latter case, the arguments already advanced would still apply, since the trusses would still span in the same direction, but in the former, most of the advantages of rationalisation would be lost, since not only would three lengths of purlin be required, including one very long one running lengthways across the type (ii) (diagram 51), but the rafter sizes also would be different (diagram 52). Regarding finishes, assumed to be slates or tiles, a contribution to simplicity has already been made by aligning part of the type (ii) roof with that of the type (i) and by eliminating awkward stepping and staggering from the scheme, but this process can be taken a useful stage further by ensuring that dimensions up the plane of the roof on each side are multiples of full tile modules, and similarly those across the roof between gable and/or party walls. Since tiles overlap the walls significantly at each side, or are masked by ridge tiles and verges, the argument about tolerance incompatibility between tiles and bricks would not apply with great force, but it is nevertheless easier to adjust the module of the brickwork in the walls than that of the tiles. For this reason, it would be a useful exercise during design to project down onto the planning grid the horizontal effect of a roof laid out to full tile modules and to adjust the shell dimensions accordingly.

**Openings: windows and doors** Buildability in masonry construction is assisted if openings are kept regular and repetitive and spaced apart from each other by brick modules. The latter point is well understood by most designers, but often this does not prevent them from selecting window shapes and combinations which negate many of the advantages gained.

The first point to be considered, once the amount of daylight, view and privacy have been decided, is where to locate the openings in the walls and what sizes and shapes the openings should be. Fortunately, most windows are supplied in ranges, which both limit the number of variations and control the sizes, but it is important to consider the design of interfacing and fixing components when calculating the 'brickwork' size of the opening, especially at cill level. Diagram 53 illustrates the main points to be considered:

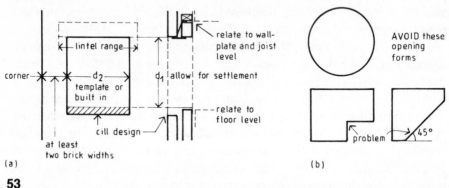

**53**

(a) shows the criteria which should be observed in all opening design, whether of windows or doors, and (b), examples of forms which should be avoided altogether if speed of assembly and economy are to be maintained. Openings should relate both to window or door frame and brickwork dimensions, allowing not only for tolerances, but also for the practicalities of assembly, such as the tendency of newly laid brickwork to settle slightly. For these reasons, building in as work proceeds is often preferred, although the use of templates is better, in that damage to finished joinery can be avoided. In brickwork openings, the cill zone is the only one where changes in tolerance can readily be accommodated, since the lintel will bear close upon the head of the frame and the bricklayer will build tightly to the jambs. For this reason, especially where a sub-cill is being used – and the provision of one is usually a good idea – this part of the opening should be completed last, once actual sizes can be measured. Other points to note are that difficulties can be caused if heads are too close to floor joists or wall plates, space having to be found for lintel, joist and wallplate bearings; if widths do not relate to lintel and cill lengths; if openings are too close, either to each other or to the wall end. Referring to diagram 53(b), these forms are achievable, owing to manufacturers having produced such components as curved cavity trays and lintels, but only with difficulty. For example, special bricks or bricks cut on the curve are required to fit round the 'bulls eye' opening, specials are necessary for the 'L' form and assembly of the splay would be easier if the angle chosen was 33° rather than 45°. Such forms were possible when labour was plentiful and cheap and are possible again thanks to new manufacturing technology and tools such as the disc cutter, but from the buildability point of view they are perverse.

### Services

In housing, the principal services to be provided are water supply, drainage, electricity, gas and telecommunications. Each has buildability factors unique to itself, but together they can present major buildability complications.

**Water**    Outside the dwelling, the supply company is responsible both for excavation of the trench and for laying the supply pipe to the internal stopcock. The complications caused when several companies supplying different services, as well as the constructor, attempt to excavate and install their mains and services at random intervals during the contract period are discussed in a companion volume[1] and the matter will not be dealt with again here, other than to reiterate that finishing trades can be adversely affected during bad weather by disturbed ground and trenching across their access routes. Within the dwelling, designers should consider the locations of storage tanks, cylinders and distribution pipework, as well as of sanitary and heating fittings. For example, pipes running through ducts designed for the purpose allow both easy installation and maintenance, provided that the ducts have removable covers, but pipes running within joisted floors, or in screeds under floor tiles, are often both difficult to install and to maintain. For these reasons, either pipes should be routed away from floors, for example on the surface or in skirting ducts, or, where their concealment is imperative, in purpose-designed spaces within the floor thickness. Similarly, access to storage tanks and cylinders is important for maintenance, which may include their removal through ceiling hatches, which must therefore be large enough for the purpose. During assembly, standardisation is helpful in allowing manufacturers to supply pre-packaged 'kits' for each major sub-assembly in the installation and in encouraging installers to develop repetitive working routines, which will speed completion. Another important point is that locations of fittings such as baths, lavatory basins and sink units should be chosen which permit not only adequate working room for the installer, but also subsequent replacement without major dismantling.

**Drainage**    House drains should be completed and tested, either before scaffolding is erected, or after it has been struck; the former is preferable.

---

[1] *Quality on Site*, Ian Ferguson and Eric Mitchell, Batsford, London, 1986.

The development of unplasticised polyvinyl chloride (Upvc) and poly-propylene drainage systems has greatly improved buildability and these sub-assemblies should be specified whenever possible and used in their simplest form. Within the dwelling, early installation of the soil and vent pipe (svp) enables wc and waste connections to be set out accurately. Connections from fittings to the stack should be short and should not run in the floor depth, which requires the forming of ducts, unless the latter serve other purposes, such as the accommodation of water pipes or heating trunking. Neither should they have to negotiate structural sub-assemblies such as piers, nor joinery fittings such as kitchen units, which will have to be cut to fit round the large diameter pipes. As with water supply pipes, straightforward design will permit the use of kits, reduce installation cost and ease maintenance.

**Electricity**   Buildability in the electrical installation of a dwelling usually implies installers running cables between meter boards and outlet points by the most direct route, cutting notches and drilling holes wherever they are needed. This economises on wiring, but not necessarily on labour, since the holes must be drilled and there can be interference with the work of other trades, especially those engaged with finishes and fittings. Furthermore, several visits to each dwelling may be necessary to complete the work. Good buildability, since it is a function of efficiency and economy, requires a rationalisation of these activities and this can be achieved, for example, by planning cable routes carefully, balancing the most direct line against co-ordination with other trades' work, and by designing joist layouts, skirtings, ceiling cornices and partition drops in an integrated way, so that 'one visit' installation is possible. That this can pay dividends has been demonstrated by work both at the Building Research Establishment[1] and by the National Building Agency in Scotland.[2] On the other hand, in a large scheme such as the one being studied, there may be sufficient dwellings in various stages of completion to enable tradesmen to work round a group more or less continuously, since each time they complete a 'cycle', they will be able to carry their work a stage further: the principle of the extensive workplace will apply (chapter 7).

**Gas**   Most of the points made about water and electricity also apply to the gas installation. Although equal care must be taken with route planning and especially, since relatively large diameter pipes are used, with the designing of ducts, the installation is much less extensive than with the water supply and complexity can often be reduced further by keeping

[1] 'The rationalisation of services in timber-frame housing in Faversham'; Building Research Establishment Internal Note N24/82; BRE/DOE, London, 1982.
[2] 'Productivity and the design team'; Anderson/Bailey; National Building Agency, Edinburgh, 1981.

outlet points, typically at the heater unit, cooker point and a focal point fire in the living area, compactly sited.

**Telecommunications** With the rapid development of communications systems, adequate facilities must be allowed in dwellings for items such as telephones, computer links, cable television and even for satellite TV aerials and, within the next few years, fibre optic cabling. Although cables are flexible and of small diameter, their distribution within the dwelling may be widespread. In buildability in use terms, this is a good argument for providing some redundancy in the spaces available for cables within the structure and finishes and for good access to those spaces via covers and easily demountable fittings and finishes.

**General** In buildability terms, services are often the last item to be considered. It is assumed by both designers and constructors that routes can be found round and through the obstructions caused by structure and finishes and that services' installers will be endlessly accommodating in this respect. This is very far from being the case and it is as important in dwellings as in the multi-storey framed building studied earlier to plan all the service routes and spaces together in an integrated way and to allow sufficient room within the structural and finishes sub-assemblies for straightforward installation and maintenance.

### Finishings and fittings
**Partitions** Partitions may be structural or non-structural and in buildability terms it is better if the former are avoided: they complicate the assembly sequence and obstruct work at ground floor level (in a two-storey dwelling). Wherever possible, in other words, it is better to clear-span joists onto external or party walls, or at least to carry proper loadbearing walls up through the structure to roof level, as shown in diagram 51. Non-structural partitions are usually of one of three types: blockwork, studwork or hollow-cored plasterboard-faced. Although blockwork performs well acoustically and as a support for heavy fittings, it is laborious to assemble and requires the introduction of 'wet' materials into a building which is already drying out. Trades much prefer, also, to have large, clear spaces within which to work and for this reason are happier with the lightweight types, which can be assembled quickly once the shell has been lined out and face-fixed to surfaces which are virtually complete. In buildability terms, the proprietary plasterboard-faced types are even better than studwork: a separate frame, assembled from many small components, is not required and openings can be formed wherever needed, even after erection, with the minimum of timber supports.

**Plasters, plasterboards and linings**   These are sensitive materials and components, hygroscopic and easily damaged. They are not ideal, therefore, in buildability terms, but because of their low cost and wide distribution, they have virtually no competitors. Plasters and plastering should be avoided, or at least confined to skim-coating, since, like blockwork, they introduce water and mess into buildings which are drying out; this in turn causes delay to following trades. The issue of plasterboard modules has already been discussed: theoretically, a shell whose internal dimensions corespond to plasterboard modules minimises off-cutting and waste. Unfortunately, tolerance incompatibility may make this ideal arrangement hard to achieve and for this reason a shell dimensioned on plan to these modules, but battened out to take dry-lining boards, will be a more practical solution: any error in the brickwork, unless it is gross, should be concealed by the depths of the battens (diagram 54):

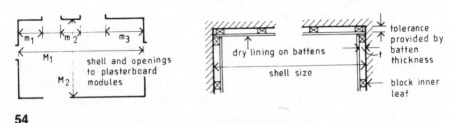

**54**

The situation is a little different when it comes to vertical modules. Although, once again, it is sensible to dimension for minimal waste, in fact tolerance is provided by the skirting and, possibly, by a ceiling cove. The important calculation here is whether the saving in labour through not having to trim boards down to a minimal floor to ceiling height is offset by the cost of laying an extra course of bricks. Note in both cases, however, that the provision of voids behind dry linings, skirtings and coves can serve the cause of buildability in the services installation referred to earlier: careful design may solve several interdependent problems simultaneously.

**Joinery and fittings**   So traditional are joinery forms and details, that it is hard to argue for change solely on the grounds of buildability. For example, architraves and skirtings are practical items, but they can be modified usefully to make assembly easier. In the former case, one piece frames are possible, cut with a deep rebate on the back edge. Frames are erected first so that doors are accurately located, especially in relation to each other, then partitions are slid into the rebate, thereby saving the assembly operation of fixing the architraves. Skirtings are too useful to dispense with, since not only do they prevent damage to the lower wall, but also they mask the joint between floor and wall finishes. Their usefulness can be enhanced as referred to earlier, however, by designing them so that they serve as ducts or cableways. Other joinery items which repay attention from the buildability viewpoint are kitchen units, shelving and storage fittings and the profiling of timberwork which supports decoration. Kitchen units, being precisely fabricated, may not fit into the spaces provided for them in masonry shells, another instance of tolerance incompatibility: in 'U' or 'L'-shaped arrangements a short length of worktop inserted into a run of units can easily be cut to the exact size required. Shelving should be simple in form, not having to be cut laboriously round pipes for example, and easily removable where access for maintenance is likely to be required. The location of heavy fittings should be carefully plotted on wall elevations during design so that bearers of adequate strength can be provided in the correct positions. Finally, timber profiles should be simple, related to the type and size of decorating tools, and pencil-rounded on the edges to allow paint to adhere properly.

**General points on finishes**   Wherever possible, components and sub-assemblies should be self-finished: site finishing takes time and is relatively expensive. This is especially true of floors and some wall surfaces. Screeds, for example, are messy, delay completion and are of doubtful durability unless very carefully mixed and laid. Unfortunately, the persistent liking for thermoplastic floor tiles requires an unblemished sub-floor and this may not be achievable with power-floating or early grinding carried out early in the contract when damage from subsequent building work is still possible. The answer is to choose an alternative and less sensitive floor finish, such as carpeting on chipboard. Wall tiles are another contentious area: although appreciated by most occupiers, their rigorous module requires accurate setting out and precise cutting and fixing, especially round window cills. Designers should allow for this and be especially careful to avoid awkward angles, rebates and edges, and resist the temptation to set socket outlets and switch plates into the tiled surface. Generally, as in the discipline of buildability as a whole, the way to achieve good finishes is to review what are available, compare them with what are required and then consider how the right results may be achieved practically, efficiently and economically.

# APPENDIX 1: Case Study
# 1 Tolerances

The following example illustrates some of the problems which occur when a joint is being assembled on site from a number of different components. The building in which the joint occurred had a medium-rise, multi-storey frame consisting of a mixture of in situ and precast columns and precast beams, with proprietary cladding panels and column facings in brickwork. For the purposes of this study, the layout of the building is unimportant, except to note that the in situ columns occurred at the corners, with precast columns spaced at structural bay widths between them. The joint as designed is illustrated in diagram A1/1.

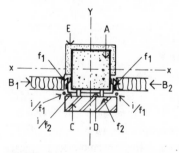

KEY

A: precast concrete column
$B_1$, $B_2$: cladding units
C: brick facing
D: dpc
E: plaster finish.

**A1/1**

In addition to these primary components, there were a number of interfacing and fixing components:

i/$f_1$: mastic seal
i/$f_2$: mortar bedding to dpc
$f_1$: spacer and cladding fixing
$f_2$: brickwork ties.

Altogether, five primary, two interfacing and two fixing components were needed to assemble each joint when viewing it on plan; at each junction between columns and beams, additional components were needed and the assembly method had to be altered. It will be apparent that, given the number of different components, several different trades were needed to assemble the joint, each with its own special tools, plant and equipment, and that the sequence of assembly was complicated. However, the main problem was with the tolerances. If assembly is to be performed efficiently, each trade must be able to rely upon the preceding trades having assembled their particular components to the correct tolerances, within the limits of allowable deviation. In the case studied, this had not happened to some of the joints, as diagram A1/2 shows.

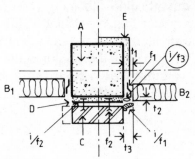

**A1/2**

Errors had occurred during assembly of three of the primary components, 'A', '$B_2$' and 'C': of 'A' because of gross differences in 'tolerance performance' between the in situ and precast frame elements, of '$B_2$' because of poor location between adjacent precast elements and of 'C' because of poor 'tolerance compatibility' between the precast column and facing brickwork. The result was that tolerances '$t_1$' , '$t_2$' and '$t_3$' were outside the limits of allowable deviation, necessitating redesign and modification of the interfacing and fixing components '$i/f_1$' and '$f_1$' and the introduction of a new interfacing component '$i/f_3$' to maintain performance of the weather seal; '$i/f_3$', of course, represented an addition to the assembly sequence.

# APPENDIX 1: Case Study 2 Assembly

Case Study 1 illustrated the tolerance problems which occurred when errors in the assembly of a complex joint were made. This Case Study examines these assembly errors in more detail and demonstrates how a proper understanding of buildability would have enabled most of them to be avoided.

The joint as designed is illustrated in diagram A1/1 (Case Study 1). It consisted of five primary, two interfacing and two fixing components. To assemble these components and to *convert* them to part of the sub-assembly forming the frame and cladding of the building, *adaptation* was necessary:

'A':      Adaptation by *omission* (drilling holes) and preparing surfaces to receive finishes

'$B_1$','$B_2$': Adaptation by *omission* (drilling holes)

'C':      No adaptation necessary to effect bond between itself and fixing component '$f_2$'

'D':      Adaptation by *omission* (cutting to length to fit round component 'A' and forming holes to allow penetration by fixing component '$f_2$')

'E':      Adaptation by *specification* to ensure chemical bonds with 'A'

'$i/f_1$': Adaptation by *specification* to ensure chemical bonds with '$B_1$', '$B_2$' and 'C'

'$i/f_2$': Adaptation by *specification* to ensure chemical bonds with 'A' and 'D'

'$f_1$':  Adaptation by *omission* and *addition* to effect connections between 'A', '$B_1$', '$B_2$'

'$f_2$':  Possible adaptation by *omission* (cutting to length) to effect connection between 'A' and 'C'.

Once the components had been prepared and converted, they had to be assembled into the joint. The following analysis shows what was involved:

| Compt | Trade Skill | Principal tools, plant, equipment | Erection sequence | Tolerance compatibility/criticality | Conversion On/Off site |
|---|---|---|---|---|---|
| A | Precast frame erector (sub/c) | Mobile crane | (1) | Compat: $B_1, B_2$ <br> Critical: $B_1, B_2$ | Off |
| $B_1 B_2$ | Cladding erector (sub/c) | Scaffolding; Fixed/mobile cr | (2) | Compat: A <br> Critical: A, C | Off |
| C | Bricklayer | Scaffolding; Fixed/mobile cr | (6) | Compat: A <br> Critical: A, $B_1 B_2$ | Off |
| D | Bricklayer | Scaffolding | (5) | Compat: A, i/$f_2$ <br> Critical: A, C | On |
| E | Plasterer | Internal lift | (8) | Compat: <br> Critical: Unimportant | On |
| i/$f_1$ | Site labour | Scaffolding | (7) | Compat: Unimportant <br> Critical: $B_1, B_2, C$ | On |
| i/$f_2$ | Bricklayer | Scaffolding | (4) | Compat: <br> Critical: Unimportant | On |
| $f_1$ | Cladding erector (sub/c) | Scaffolding | (2) | Compat: A, $B_1, B_2$ <br> Critical: A, $B_1, B_2$ | On |
| $f_2$ | Bricklayer | Scaffolding | (3) | Compat: C <br> Critical: C | On |

**Table A1/1**

Four separate trades were needed to carry out the assembly sequence, with assistance from site labour to apply the mastic seals, mix mortar and plaster, etc. Of the four trades, three were sub-contractors (one, labour only). As table A1/1 shows, the sequence of assembly had to be carefully planned, which required good organisation, for example to ensure that components were available when required, that sub-contractor pro-grammes were coordinated and that scaffolding was erected as soon as the frame was complete. In practice, a number of problems occurred, some serious (diagram A1/3):

(i)  The mixture of in situ and precast columns (Case Study 1), with their poor tolerance compatibility, forced errors in the spacing of the columns. This made it difficult to fit the cladding units, 'B', into the spaces between column faces, 'A', tolerances departing from their allowable deviations and making it either impossible or difficult to use fixing components '$f_1$'. The constraints upon the use of this fixing component are illustrated in diagram A1/3.

Both '$d_1$' and '$d_2$' could vary up to the limits of allowable deviation, variation being accommodated by slotted holes in '$f_1$' and spacers in front of and behind it; alternative variations could be allowed for by drilling hole '$h_1$' on site, although this would not have been desirable for structural reasons. It should be noted, also, that because the fixing into '$h_2$' would be inaccessible once the cladding component '$B_1$' was placed in position, that fixing had to be either tight and permanent, or secure but free to rotate about the screw, which would have facilitated

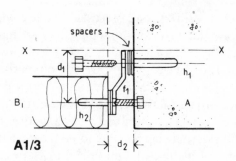

**A1/3**

the location and fixing of the screw into '$h_1$'. Other points are that any packing behind the screw at '$h_2$' could not be altered once '$B_1$' was in place, all final adjustment having to be made at '$h_1$', that only the '$h_1$' end of '$f_1$' needed to have a slotted hole – for the same reason – and that the allowable deviation should not have been so great that it was impossible to get a tool onto the screw into '$h_1$' (controlled by the position of hole '$h_2$').

(ii) Owing to the inaccurate position of '$B_2$' and the resulting large gap between the end of '$B_2$' and the side face of 'A', a large number of spacers had to be provided at the inner end of '$f_1$' to effect a fixing. This prejudiced both the weather-tightness of the interface and the ability of the plaster finish, 'E', to conceal the fixing.

(iii) Coincidentally, the bricklayer found it impossible, because of the dimensional constraints of the brick bond selected, to build the brick facing sufficiently wide to master the interfaces between '$B_1$', '$B_2$' and 'A'.

(iv) The bricklayer had not returned the vertical DPC, 'D', round the flanking faces of 'A'.

(v) The result was the necessity of introducing a weather seal, '$i/f_1$' of modified specification and an additional weather seal, '$i/f_3$', to reduce the risk of water penetrating through the large gap between 'A' and '$B_2$'.

Had the principles of good buildability been applied to the problems presented by this joint, better solutions could have been found. The principles of tolerance compatibility and criticality have already been discussed and it is apparent that gross deviations in tolerances were largely responsible for the remedial measures referred to in (v). In addition, however, the quality of assembly was poor, as in the inaccurate location of '$B_1$' and '$B_2$' either side of 'A' and in the failure to return the DPC, 'D', round the flanking faces of 'A'. Even more important, there was a misunderstanding by the designer of how brickwork relates dimensionally to other components. From this, a number of conclusions can be drawn:

(a)  It is unwise to mix in situ and precast concrete components in the same sub-assembly: the tolerances to which they are made are often widely different, ie their tolerance compatibility is poor.

(b)  Close supervision of personnel carrying out early assembly activities may be necessary when these activities are critical to the accuracy and performance of later activities: in this case, it was essential that '$B_1$' and '$B_2$' were correctly plumbed and aligned in the frame to enable external and internal components to be fixed accurately.

(c)  Owing to the difficulty of building frames to close and consistent tolerances, it is usually better to fix cladding units to the outer face of the frame, rather than between its return faces (A1/4):

tolerance not critical                                    tolerance critical

**A1/4**

(d)  Four separate trades were needed to assemble the joint, plus casual site labour, requiring careful and extensive supervision. The trades were working to dissimilar tolerances and had poor appreciations of each other's problems. A better solution altogether would have been to omit the brick cladding ('C') to the column face, together with its attendant dpc ('D'), fixings ('$f_2$') and seals and bedding ('$i/f_1$', '$i/f_2$'). The cladding components ('$B_1$', '$B_2$') would then have been fixed to the outer faces of the columns, with the advantages noted in (c):

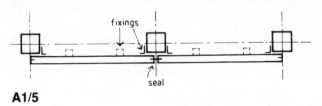

fixings

seal

**A1/5**

The effect of this upon buildability would have been to reduce the number of trades from four to three and the number of assembly activities from eight to four: frame erection, cladding fixing, cladding weather seal fixing and plastering.

(e)  Scaffolding is expensive to hire and delays assembly whilst it is being erected. Had the cladding fixings '$f_1$' been designed to permit internal fixing of the exterior located panels (a), a simple hanging scaffold or hydraulic platform would have sufficed to fix the weather seals.

# APPENDIX 2:
# Assembling a timber floor

This example illustrates and describes an approach to designing for buildability. It shows how the principles of conversion and adaptation are applied to the design of a timber first floor, with timber joists spanning onto an intermediate rolled steel joist (RSJ), and how, once the design is complete, a method statement can be prepared for inclusion in the documentation.

The general arrangement of the floor is shown in diagram A2/1(a):

The decision to use a RSJ resulted from an analysis of the economic spans of timber floor joists and the aesthetic requirement that there should be no downstand beam visible in the ground floor. '$d_1$' and '$d_2$' represent the effective spans of the timber joists and '$d_3$' that of the RSJ; both types of joist are built in to masonry external walls where one does not bear upon the other. Analysis of the characteristics of the steel and timber joists shows that, whereas the latter can be adapted by omission of material, at 'x' (A2/1(b)), this is not possible with the former, except in its length. It is possible, therefore, to fit the timber joists snugly into the web of the RSJ and to space parallel joists apart at the distance required ('$d_4$') for the load and span (A2/1(c)). Since the joists are unlikely to be a completely tight fit, it might well be desirable to fit spacer blocks between them to prevent them moving or twisting, these simply

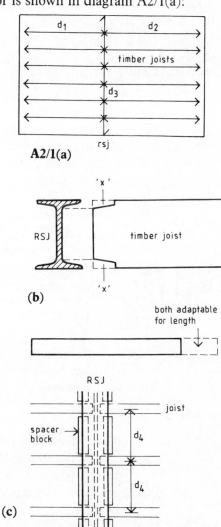

**A2/1(a)**

**(b)**

**(c)**

being hammered into position and
skew-nailed into the adjacent joists.
At the wall end, both RSJ and
timber joists would be spaced,
levelled and bedded into the inner
leaf blockwork.

Having agreed the design, it is now possible to prepare a method
statement for the assembly sequence (A2/2):

| Sub-assembly or component | Sequence of assembly | Function and performance | Cost |
|---|---|---|---|
| | (1) Raise walls to 'h' and level | Ensure correct floor/ceiling ht | – |
| | (2) Cut '$c_1$' (RSJ) to length, place in position and level with 'i/$f_1$' | Specify RSJ section and bearing | £x |
| | (3) Cut '$c_2$' (timber joists) to length, adapt to fit by trimming one end, place in position in web of '$c_1$' and level with 'i/$f_2$' | Specify joist size, spacing, bearing | 'n' joists at £x/ metre run |
| | (4) Cut 'i/$f_3$' to joist spacing and nail in position in web of '$c_1$' | Specify size of blocks and nails | 'n' blocks at £x/ block |
| | (5) Build in 'i/$f_4$' (beam filling) at wall end | Specify blocks | £x for cutting and fixing |
| | (6) Fix strutting, wedges, mild steel straps. | Specify type, size, spacing of straps. | £x for compo-nents |

Note that the discipline of writing such a statement forces the designer to consider the sequence of assembly and how, in a thoroughly practical sense, the work must be carried out. If at the same time he keeps in mind the cardinal principles of tolerance, variety reduction and repetition, he will see that, for example, primary component '$C_1$' (RSJ) should be placed at mid-span to avoid having two sizes of '$C_2$' (timber joists), that the spacing ('$d_4$') of the joists should not vary, so that only one size of spacer block will be needed and that '$d_4$' should, if possible, equal the length of one insulation block ($i/f_4$), so that this will not have to be cut for the beam filling. He will also consider ways of reducing the number of different interfacing components and fixings and of making these as simple as possible: for example, the spacer blocks ($i/f_3$) might be fabricated from off-cuts from the timber joists, which would therefore be supplied oversize, and interfacing components '$i/f_i$' and '$i/f_2$ might be eliminated by an instruction to the bricklayer to make up levels using only coursing 'bricks' and by a design decision to accept a slight variation in floor to ceiling height.

# Further reading

ANDERSON, WE ROBERTS, JJ and WATT, P, Efficient Masonry House-building, Cement and Concrete Association, 1985

BARRIE, DONALD S and PAULSON, BOYD C, *Professional Construction Management*, McGraw-Hill, 1984

BEAVER, P, *The Crystal Palace*, Evelyn, London, 1970

BUILDING EDUCATION, 'Faster Building for Industry', HMSO, 1983, July

BRE/UMIST, 'Designing for Production', lecturers' notes, transparencies, slide pack and video-cassette' BRE/DoE, Garston, 1985

FORBES, WS and STJERNSTEDT, R, 'The Finchampstead Report', BRE Current Paper No. 23, HMSO, 1972

HERBERT, G, 'Pioneers of prefabrication: the British contribution in the 19th century', Hopkins University Press, Baltimore, 1978

NATIONAL BUILDING AGENCY, 'A study of alternative methods of house construction', Special Report No. 30, NBA, Edinburgh, 1968

SAINT, ANDREW, *The Image of the Architect*, Yale University Press, 1983.

# Index